MEI STRUCTURED MATHEMATICS

SECOND EDITION

Pure Mathematics 5

Terry Heard
David Martin

Series Editor: Roger Porkess

Hodder & Stoughton

A MEMBER OF THE HODDER HEADLINE GROUP

Acknowledgements

We are grateful to the following companies, institutions and individuals who have given permission to reproduce photographs in this book. Every effort has been made to trace and acknowledge ownership of copyright. The publishers will be glad to make suitable arrangements with any copyright holders whom it has not been possible to contact.

Photographs:

Claude Nuridsany and Marie Perennou/Science Photo Library (24)

Astrid and Hanns-Frieder Michler/Science Photo Library (37)

Mathematical Snapshots by H. Steinhaus New edition 1960 © 1950 OUP New York (64)

Martin Dohrn/Science Photo Library (89)

Mr. K.C.D. Shuttleworth/Bupa Hospitals Ltd. for St. Thomas, Lithotriptier Centre (136)

Department of Prints and Drawings, British Museum (140)

Orders: please contact Bookpoint Ltd, 130 Milton Park, Abingdon, Oxon OX14 4SB. Telephone: (44) 01235 827720, Fax: (44) 01235 400454. Lines are open from 9.00–6.00, Monday to Saturday, with a 24 hour message answering service. You can also order through our website www.hodderheadline.co.uk

British Library Cataloguing in Publication Data
A catalogue record for this title is available from the The British Library

ISBN 0 340 846917

First published 1996
Second edition published 2003
Impression number   10 9 8 7 6 5 4 3 2 1
Year   2008 2007 2006 2005 2004 2003

Copyright © 1996, 2003 Terry Heard, David Martin

Typeset by Pantek Arts Ltd, Maidstone, Kent.
Printed in Great Britain for Hodder & Stoughton Educational, a division of Hodder Headline Plc, 338 Euston Road, London NW1 3BH by Martins the Printers Ltd, Berwick upon Tweed.

MEI Structured Mathematics

Mathematics is not only a beautiful and exciting subject in its own right but also one that underpins many other branches of learning. It is consequently fundamental to the success of a modern economy.

MEI Structured Mathematics is designed to increase substantially the number of people taking the subject post-GCSE, by making it accessible, interesting and relevant to a wide range of students.

It is a credit accumulation scheme based on 45 hour modules which may be taken individually or aggregated to give Advanced Subsidiary (AS) and Advanced GCE (A Level) qualifications in Mathematics, Further Mathematics and related subjects (like Statistics). The modules may also be used to obtain credit towards other types of qualification.

The course is examined by OCR (previously the Oxford and Cambridge Schools Examination Board) with examinations held in January and June each year.

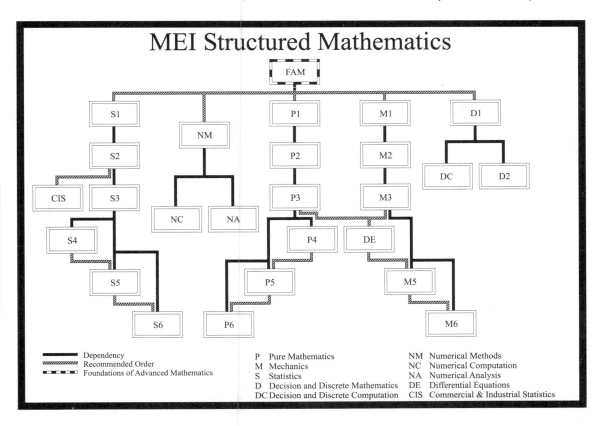

This is one of the series of books written to support the course. Its position within the whole scheme can be seen in the diagram above.

Mathematics in Education and Industry is a curriculum development body which aims to promote the links between Education and Industry in Mathematics at secondary level, and to produce relevant examination and teaching syllabuses and support material. Since its foundation in the 1960s, MEI has provided syllabuses for GCSE (or O Level), Additional Mathematics and A Level.

For more information about MEI Structured Mathematics or other syllabuses and materials, write to MEI Office, Albion House, Market Place, Westbury, Wiltshire, BA13 3DE.

Introduction

This is the fifth of the series of books covering the pure mathematics components of the MEI Structured Mathematics course. It is supported by additional on-line materials available through the MEI distance learning programme. For further details please e-mail the MEI office: Office@mei.org.uk.

This book takes you well into Further Mathematics territory. This does not mean that the new ideas presented here are necessarily difficult, but at this level it is appropriate to work on the basis of reasonably reliable technique (so you should be prepared to complete the details for yourself in some of the worked examples), and to be clear about proving results (or, occasionally, realising that a proof cannot be given yet). So, for example, in the Algebra chapter care is taken to justify some important results which you may have taken as 'obvious' so far. The frequent Activities and ❓ Discussion Points are an essential part of the course, designed to help your understanding. Hints and answers for these (and for all the exercises) are given, but it is important to tackle these tasks seriously before turning to the back of the book!

The Complex numbers, Calculus and Power series chapters build on the work of earlier components. The optional Appendix draws together these ideas to give a glimpse of mathematical life beyond the examination specification. There is considerable emphasis on geometry in this book, most obviously in Geometry with polar co-ordinates and the two Conics chapters, but also in Complex numbers. The importance of geometry has been somewhat neglected in recent years, and we hope that the full treatment given here will enable you to feel at home in this rich and powerful field.

In the first edition we recorded with pleasure our indebtedness to family, friends, colleagues and students (not mutually exclusive categories!), particularly Diana Cowey, Ray Dunnett and Mike Jones, for their help in many ways during the writing and production of the book. For this second edition of *Pure Mathematics 5*, which has been prepared by Terry Heard, several chapters have been rearranged or rewritten (including contributions from Richard Lissaman) to improve the flow of ideas; recent examination questions have been added and surplus material removed. In all of this the help of Charlie Stripp, Richard Lissaman, Mike Jones and Penny Nicholson is gratefully acknowledged.

Terry Heard and David Martin

Contents

Algebra

In mathematics it is new ways of looking at old things that seem to be the most prolific sources of far-reaching discoveries.

Eric Temple Bell, 1951

❓ Figure 1.1(a) shows a cube of side x from which another cube of side y has been removed. Figure 1.1(b) is an exploded view of the same solid. Explain how it illustrates that $x^3 - y^3 \equiv (x-y)(x^2 + xy + y^2)$.

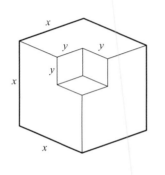

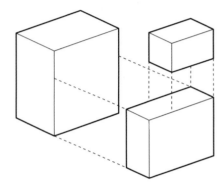

Figure 1.1(a)   **(b)**

Identities

During your work in mathematics you will have seen and used statements (known as *identities*) such as the one above, as well as the following.

1 $\ -(1-x) \equiv x-1$

2 $\ (x+y)^2 \equiv x^2 + 2xy + y^2$

3 $\ \dfrac{a^2 - b^2}{a+b} \equiv a-b$

The symbol $\equiv$ means 'is identically equal to'; it is used to emphasise that these statements are true for all values of the variables for which the functions involved are defined. Statements 1 and 2 are true for all values of x and y. Statement 3 is true for all values of a and b, provided $a+b \neq 0$.

Distinguish carefully between equations and identities.

- All possible values of the variable (or variables) will satisfy an identity, provided only that they are in the domains of all the relevant functions. The identity $(x-1)^2 \equiv x^2 - 2x + 1$ (for example) is true for all values of x. It does not make sense to try to solve something you recognise as an identity.

- There will be some values of the variable (or variables) which do not satisfy an equation. The equation $x^2 - 7x + 12 = 0$ (for example) is only satisfied by $x = 3$ or 4.

Whenever you see the symbol $\equiv$ you can be sure you are dealing with an identity. You may also meet some statements which look like equations (using the symbol $=$) but are in fact identities.

You will also be familiar with trigonometrical identities such as

$$\sin(-\theta) \equiv -\sin\theta \text{ (true for all values of } \theta)$$

and $\sec^2\theta \equiv \tan^2\theta + 1$ (true for all values of θ for which $\tan\theta$ and $\sec\theta$ are defined) but this chapter is concerned only with polynomial identities (in which the only functions used are polynomial functions) and identities that can be derived from them.

Polynomials

Much of the following terminology will probably be familiar. A *polynomial of degree n* is any expression which can be put in the form

$$c_n x^n + c_{n-1} x^{n-1} + c_{n-2} x^{n-2} + \cdots + c_1 x + c_0 \qquad \text{where } c_n \neq 0.$$

Each term is the product of a *coefficient* (c_r) and x^r where r is a positive integer or zero. This may also be described as a polynomial *of order n*; $c_n x^n$ is known as the *leading term*; c_n, the coefficient of the leading term, is known as the *leading coefficient*; c_0, the coefficient of x^0, is known as the *constant term*.

The *zero polynomial* is the polynomial which has all its coefficients equal to zero. Notice the distinction between a polynomial of degree zero and the zero polynomial:

- a polynomial of degree zero has all its coefficients equal to zero except the constant term: it is also known as a *constant polynomial*

- the zero polynomial has all its coefficients equal to zero: its degree is undefined.

Adding, subtracting and multiplying polynomials will be familiar. For example, if $P(x) \equiv 3x^2 + 4x - 5$ and $Q(x) \equiv 2x^2 + 4x - 3$ then

$$P(x) + Q(x) \equiv 5x^2 + 8x - 8;$$
$$P(x) - Q(x) \equiv x^2 - 2;$$
$$P(x)Q(x) \equiv (3x^2 + 4x - 5)(2x^2 + 4x - 3) \equiv 6x^4 + 20x^3 - 3x^2 + 32x + 15.$$

ACTIVITY

$P(x)$ and $Q(x)$ are polynomials of degree m and n respectively.

(i) If $m \neq n$ what can you say about the degree of
   (a) $P(x) + Q(x)$
   (b) $P(x) - Q(x)$
   (c) $P(x)Q(x)$?

(ii) Repeat (i) when $m = n$.

You will have noticed that the product of a polynomial of degree m with a polynomial of degree n is a polynomial of degree $m + n$. This property holds even when one (or both) of the polynomials is of degree 0, but it would not hold if any finite degree were attached to the zero polynomial.

Polynomial division

Consider the following division process in which the polynomial

$P(x) \equiv x^3 - 4x^2 + 7x - 12$ is divided by $x - 2$.

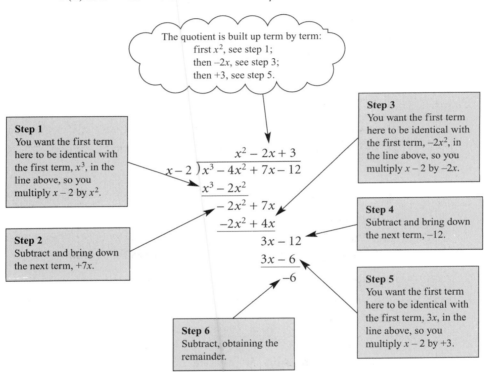

The quotient is built up term by term:
first x^2, see step 1;
then $-2x$, see step 3;
then $+3$, see step 5.

Step 1
You want the first term here to be identical with the first term, x^3, in the line above, so you multiply $x - 2$ by x^2.

Step 2
Subtract and bring down the next term, $+7x$.

Step 3
You want the first term here to be identical with the first term, $-2x^2$, in the line above, so you multiply $x - 2$ by $-2x$.

Step 4
Subtract and bring down the next term, -12.

Step 5
You want the first term here to be identical with the first term, $3x$, in the line above, so you multiply $x - 2$ by $+3$.

Step 6
Subtract, obtaining the remainder.

$$\begin{array}{r} x^2 - 2x + 3 \\ x - 2 \overline{)\, x^3 - 4x^2 + 7x - 12} \\ x^3 - 2x^2 \\ -2x^2 + 7x \\ -2x^2 + 4x \\ 3x - 12 \\ 3x - 6 \\ -6 \end{array}$$

The division tells you that when $P(x) \equiv x^3 - 4x^2 + 7x - 12$ (known as the *dividend*) is divided by $x - 2$ (known as the *divisor*) the quotient is $x^2 - 2x + 3$, and the remainder is -6. You can write this result as the identity

$$\frac{x^3 - 4x^2 + 7x - 12}{x - 2} \equiv x^2 - 2x + 3 + \frac{-6}{x - 2}. \qquad ①$$

However it is probably better to write it as

$$P(x) \equiv x^3 - 4x^2 + 7x - 12 \equiv (x - 2)(x^2 - 2x + 3) - 6 \qquad ②$$

since identity ① is valid for all x except $x = 2$ while identity ② is valid for all values of x. Note the pattern familiar from the division of numbers:

$$\text{dividend} = \text{divisor} \times \text{quotient} + \text{remainder}.$$

Notice that $P(2) = 8 - 16 + 14 - 12 = -6 =$ the remainder. This is no coincidence, as substituting $x = 2$ in ② will show. This property forms the subject of the remainder theorem on page 5.

Division by a quadratic or cubic polynomial is performed in much the same way as division by a linear polynomial. The following example illustrates this.

EXAMPLE 1.1

Find the quotient and remainder when $6x^4 - 32x^2 + 7$ is divided by $3x^2 + 3x - 1$ and write out the corresponding identity.

SOLUTION

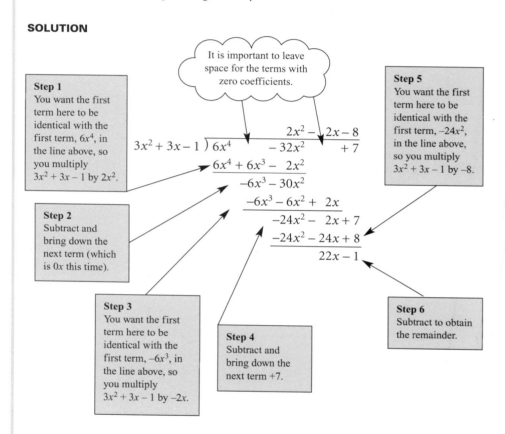

Step 1
You want the first term here to be identical with the first term, $6x^4$, in the line above, so you multiply $3x^2 + 3x - 1$ by $2x^2$.

Step 2
Subtract and bring down the next term (which is $0x$ this time).

Step 3
You want the first term here to be identical with the first term, $-6x^3$, in the line above, so you multiply $3x^2 + 3x - 1$ by $-2x$.

Step 4
Subtract and bring down the next term $+7$.

Step 5
You want the first term here to be identical with the first term, $-24x^2$, in the line above, so you multiply $3x^2 + 3x - 1$ by -8.

Step 6
Subtract to obtain the remainder.

It is important to leave space for the terms with zero coefficients.

$$3x^2 + 3x - 1 \overline{\smash{)}\,6x^4 \qquad - 32x^2 \qquad + 7}$$

quotient: $2x^2 - 2x - 8$

$6x^4 + 6x^3 - 2x^2$
$-6x^3 - 30x^2$
$-6x^3 - 6x^2 + 2x$
$-24x^2 - 2x + 7$
$-24x^2 - 24x + 8$
$22x - 1$

The quotient is $2x^2 - 2x - 8$; the remainder is $22x - 1$.

The identity is $6x^4 - 32x^2 + 7 \equiv (3x^2 + 3x - 1)(2x^2 - 2x - 8) + 22x - 1$.

EXERCISE 1A

1 Divide $x^2 + 2x + 1$ by $x + 3$ and state the identity that is established.

2 Divide $x^3 + 4x^2 - 7x + 2$ by $x + 3$ and state the identity that is established.

3 Divide $x^4 + 6x^2 + 12$ by $x - 5$ and state the identity that is established.

4 Divide $2x^3 + 3x^2 - 5x + 7$ by $2x + 1$ and state the identity that is established.

5 For each of the following pairs of polynomials, divide $P(x)$ by $f(x)$ and express your result in the form of an identity.

(i) $P(x) \equiv 2x^4 - 3x^2 - 5x + 7, \quad f(x) = x^2 + 2$

(ii) $P(x) \equiv 4x^5 - 2x^4 - 2x^3 + x^2 - 3x + 2, \quad f(x) = 2x^2 - 3$

(iii) $P(x) \equiv x^4 + 2x^3 - 5x^2 + 4x + 9, \quad f(x) = x^2 - x + 3$

(iv) $P(x) \equiv 3x^4 - 8x^3 + 29x^2 + 21, \quad f(x) = x^2 - x + 7$

(v) $P(x) \equiv x^4 + 3x - 1, \quad f(x) = x^2 - 2$

(vi) $P(x) \equiv x^4 - 1, \quad f(x) = x - 1$

6 (i) In each case below, divide $P(x)$ by $(x - a)$ and establish an identity.

(a) $P(x) \equiv x^2 - a^2$

(b) $P(x) \equiv x^3 - a^3$

(c) $P(x) \equiv x^4 - a^4$

(ii) Show, by polynomial division, by algebraic manipulation or by summing a suitable geometric progression, that

$$x^n - a^n \equiv (x - a)(x^{n-1} + ax^{n-2} + a^2x^{n-3} + \cdots + a^{n-2}x + a^{n-1}).$$

7 (i) Show that $x + a$ is a factor of $x^3 + a^3$.

(ii) Factorise $x^3 + a^3$ and $x^5 + a^5$.

(iii) Prove, by substituting $-a$ for a in the identity in Question 6 part (ii) that, provided n is odd,

$$x^n + a^n \equiv (x + a)(x^{n-1} - ax^{n-2} + a^2x^{n-3} - \cdots - a^{n-2}x + a^{n-1}).$$

8 Given that $f(x) = (x - 3)g(x) + x + 2$, find the remainder when $f(x)$ is divided by $(x - 3)$.

9 Given that $f(x) = (x - 3)g(x) + 2$, find the remainder when $[f(x)]^2$ is divided by $(x - 3)$.

10 Given that $f(x) = (x - 3)(x + 2)g(x) + 2x + 3$, find the remainder when $[f(x)]^2$ is divided by $(x - 3)(x + 2)$.

11 Suppose that $f(x) = (x + 2)^2 g(x) + rx + s$. If $f(-2) = 3$ and $f'(-2) = 1$ find r and s.

The remainder theorem

When a polynomial is divided by a linear expression (i.e. a polynomial of degree 1) the remainder is a number. It is possible to find this remainder without working through the details of the division. The following theorem shows how.

THE REMAINDER THEOREM

If a polynomial $P(x)$ is divided by $x - a$ the remainder is $P(a)$.

PROOF

When dividing a polynomial by a linear expression the remainder is clearly a constant (possibly zero). Suppose dividing $P(x)$ by $x - a$ gives quotient $Q(x)$ and remainder R, so that

$$P(x) \equiv (x - a)Q(x) + R.$$

Putting $x = a$ gives $\qquad P(a) = 0 \times Q(a) + R \qquad$ so that $R = P(a)$.

EXAMPLE 1.2

Find the remainder when $P(x) \equiv 3x^4 - 5x^3 + 2x^2 - 7x + 2$ is divided by

(i) $x + 2$ (ii) $2x - 1$.

> Evaluate $P(x)$ at $x = -2$, the value which would make divisor $= 0$.

SOLUTION

(i) $P(x) \equiv (x + 2)Q_1(x) + R_1$;
putting $x = -2$: $R_1 = P(-2) = 3(-2)^4 - 5(-2)^3 + 2(-2)^2 - 7(-2) + 2 = 112$.
When $P(x)$ is divided by $x + 2$ the remainder is 112.

> Evaluate $P(x)$ at $x = \frac{1}{2}$, the value which would make divisor $= 0$.

(ii) $P(x) \equiv (2x - 1)Q_2(x) + R_2$;
putting $x = \frac{1}{2}$: $R_2 = P\left(\frac{1}{2}\right) = 3\left(\frac{1}{2}\right)^4 - 5\left(\frac{1}{2}\right)^3 + 2\left(\frac{1}{2}\right)^2 - 7\left(\frac{1}{2}\right) + 2 = -\frac{23}{16}$.
When $P(x)$ is divided by $2x - 1$ the remainder is $-\frac{23}{16}$.

The *factor theorem* is a special case of the remainder theorem: if $P(x)$ is a polynomial and $P(a) = 0$, the remainder when $P(x)$ is divided by $x - a$ is zero, and $x - a$ is a factor of polynomial $P(x)$.

There is not a generalised version of the remainder theorem which tells you the remainder when you are dividing by a polynomial of degree 2 or more.

EXAMPLE 1.3

When $P(x) \equiv x^3 + bx^2 + cx + 5$ is divided by $x - 2$ the remainder is 3. When $P(x)$ is divided by $x + 3$ the remainder is -67. Find b and c.

SOLUTION

$P(2) = 3 \quad \Rightarrow 8 + 4b + 2c + 5 = 3 \quad \Rightarrow 4b + 2c = -10$ ①
$P(-3) = -67 \Rightarrow -27 + 9b - 3c + 5 = -67 \Rightarrow 9b - 3c = -45$ ②

> It is possible to form equations ① and ② by polynomial division, but this takes much longer and there is more room for blunders.

Solving ① and ② simultaneously:

$\qquad\qquad$ ① $\Rightarrow 2b + c = -5$
$\qquad\qquad$ ② $\Rightarrow 3b - c = -15$
Adding gives: $\qquad\qquad 5b = -20$

so that $b = -4$ and $c = 3$.

1 Use the remainder theorem to find the remainder when $P(x) \equiv x^3 + 3x^2 - x - 5$ is divided by each of the following.

  (i) $x + 1$ **(ii)** $x - 1$ **(iii)** $x + 2$ **(iv)** $x - 2$ **(v)** x

2 Use the remainder theorem to find the remainder when $P(x) \equiv (x + 1)(x + 2)(2x + 6)$ is divided by each of the following.

  (i) $x + 1$ **(ii)** $x + 2$ **(iii)** $x + 3$ **(iv)** $x + 4$ **(v)** x

3 The polynomial $P(x) \equiv x^3 + ax^2 + bx + c$ leaves remainders -36, -20 and 0 on division by $x + 1$, $x + 2$ and $x + 3$ respectively. Find a, b and c and then solve the equation $P(x) = 0$.

4 **(i)** Write down an expression for the remainder when a polynomial $P(x)$ is divided by $x - a$.

When $f(x) = 2x^6 + kx^5 + 32x^2 - 26$ is divided by $(x + 1)$ the remainder is 15.

  (ii) Calculate the value of the constant k.

$f(x)$ is now divided by $(x - 2)$ giving the quotient $g(x)$ and the remainder R, so that

$$f(x) = (x - 2)g(x) + R. \qquad \qquad ①$$

  (iii) Calculate the remainder R.
  (iv) Calculate $g(-1)$.
  (v) By differentiating the identity ①, or otherwise, calculate $g(2)$.

                                                                                                    [MEI]

5 Find the remainder when $2x^3 - 5x^2 - 4x + 9$ is divided by **(i)** $x + 4$ **(ii)** $2x - 1$.

6 Show that the remainder when the polynomial $P(x)$ is divided by $ax + b$ is $P\left(-\frac{b}{a}\right)$.

7 Explain the difference between the identity $P(x) \equiv 0$ and the equation $P(x) = 0$ when $P(x) \equiv ax^2 + bx + c$.

8 When the polynomial $P(x)$ is divided by $x - a$ there is no remainder. When $P(x)$ is divided by $x - a + 1$ the quotient is $Q(x)$ and the remainder is R. Prove that $R = -Q(a)$.

9 When the polynomial $P(x)$ is divided by $(x - a)(x - b)$ the quotient is $Q(x)$ and the remainder is $rx + s$. By writing this as an identity and giving suitable values to x, find the constants r and s in terms of a, b, $P(a)$ and $P(b)$ assuming $a \neq b$.

10 When the polynomial $P(x)$ is divided by $(x - a)(x - b)$ the quotient is $Q(x)$ and there is no remainder. $P(x) = 0$ has no roots between a and b and the factors $x - a$ and $x - b$ are not repeated. Prove that $Q(a)$ and $Q(b)$ have the same sign.

11 When $P_1(x)$ is divided by $x - a$ the remainder is R. When $P_2(x)$ is divided by $x - a$ the remainder is S.

  (i)   Prove that when $P_1(x) + P_2(x)$ is divided by $x - a$ the remainder is $R + S$.
  (ii) Find the remainder when $P_1(x)P_2(x)$ is divided by $x - a$.

12 When the polynomial f(x) is divided by ($x - 2$) the remainder is 7. When f(x) is divided by ($x + 3$) the remainder is 32.

(i) When f(x) is divided by ($x - 2$)($x + 3$) the quotient is Q(x) and the remainder is $rx + s$, so that

$$f(x) = (x - 2)(x + 3)Q(x) + rx + s.$$

Find r and s.

(ii) Given that f$'$(2) = 10 find the remainder when f(x) is divided by ($x - 2$)^2.

[MEI, part]

13 When the polynomial f(x) is divided by ($x - 3$)($x + 1$), the quotient is g(x) and the remainder is $-2x + 5$ so that

$$f(x) = (x - 3)(x + 1)g(x) - 2x + 5.$$

(i) Find the remainder when
  (a) f(x) is divided by ($x - 3$)
  (b) f(x) is divided by ($x + 1$).

(ii) Find the remainder when [f(x)]^2 is divided by ($x - 3$)($x + 1$).

(iii) Given that g(3) = 4 show that f$'$(3) = 14 and find the remainder when [f(x)]^2 is divided by ($x - 3$)^2.

[MEI, part]

Extending the factor theorem

If P(x) is a polynomial, each value of x for which P(x) = 0 is called a *root* of P(x). (Some texts call such a value a *zero* of P(x).)

Suppose you want to find a cubic polynomial P(x) which has three distinct roots: 1, 2, and 3. Then by the factor theorem ($x - 1$) is a factor of P(x), and so are ($x - 2$) and ($x - 3$).

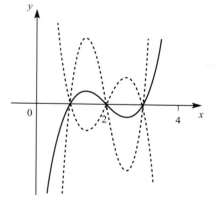

P(x) could be ($x - 1$)($x - 2$)($x - 3$)
or $5(x - 1)(x - 2)(x - 3)$
or $-2(x - 1)(x - 2)(x - 3)$

as illustrated in figure 1.2.

Figure 1.2

Although there are infinitely many possibilities for P(x), you cannot find a cubic polynomial with roots 1, 2, and 3 which cannot be expressed in the form P(x) $\equiv$ $c(x - 1)(x - 2)(x - 3)$, where c is a non-zero constant.

Extending and generalising this idea leads to the following theorem, which is proved by induction.

THEOREM

If $P(x)$ is a polynomial of degree n $(\geqslant 1)$ with n distinct roots $a_1, a_2, a_3, \ldots, a_n$ then $P(x) \equiv c(x - a_1)(x - a_2)(x - a_3)\ldots(x - a_n)$, where c is a non-zero constant.

PROOF

(i) The first stage is to show that the theorem is true for $n = 1$.
$P(x)$ is a polynomial of degree 1 with root a_1

$\Rightarrow P(x) \equiv c_1 x + c_0$, where c_1 is non-zero and $P(a_1) = 0$
$\Rightarrow c_1 a_1 + c_0 = 0$
$\Rightarrow c_0 = -c_1 a_1$.

Therefore $P(x) \equiv c_1 x - c_1 a_1 \equiv c_1(x - a_1)$ where c_1 is a non-zero constant, as required.

(ii) The next stage is to show that if the theorem is true for $n = k$ then it is also true for $n = k + 1$.

$P(x)$ is a polynomial of degree $k + 1$ with $k + 1$ distinct roots $a_1, a_2, a_3, \ldots, a_k, a_{k+1}$

$\Rightarrow P(a_{k+1}) = 0$
$\Rightarrow P(x) \equiv (x - a_{k+1})Q(x)$

applying the remainder theorem

where $Q(x)$ is a polynomial of degree k.

Putting $x = a_1$ gives $(a_1 - a_{k+1})Q(a_1) = P(a_1) = 0$;

but $a_1 - a_{k+1} \neq 0$, so $Q(a_1) = 0$. In other words a_1 is a root of $Q(x)$.

In the same way you can show that $a_2, a_3, \ldots, a_k$, are also roots of $Q(x)$.

Therefore $Q(x)$ is of degree k, with k distinct roots $a_1, a_2, a_3, \ldots, a_k$, so the theorem may be applied to $Q(x)$:

$$Q(x) \equiv c(x - a_1)(x - a_2)(x - a_3)\ldots(x - a_k), \text{ where } c \text{ is a non-zero constant.}$$

Therefore $P(x) \equiv (x - a_{k+1})Q(x) \equiv (x - a_{k+1})c(x - a_1)(x - a_2)(x - a_3)\ldots(x - a_k)$
$\equiv c(x - a_1)(x - a_2)(x - a_3)\ldots(x - a_k)(x - a_{k+1})$

where c is a non-zero constant.

From (i) and (ii) by induction the theorem holds for all positive integers n.

One immediate consequence of this theorem is that a polynomial of degree n cannot have more than n distinct roots. For if $P(x)$ is a polynomial with n distinct roots $a_1, a_2, a_3, \ldots, a_n$, then $P(x) \equiv c(x - a_1)(x - a_2)(x - a_3)\ldots(x - a_n)$, where c is a non-zero constant. If b is not one of $a_1, a_2, a_3, \ldots, a_n$, then $P(b) = c(b - a_1)(b - a_2)(b - a_3)\ldots(b - a_n) \neq 0$, so that b is not a root.

Equating coefficients

 (i) Is it possible for the graphs of two different quadratic polynomials, $P(x)$ and $Q(x)$, to intersect at three points?

(ii) Is it possible for the graphs of two different cubic polynomials, $P(x)$ and $Q(x)$, to intersect at four points?

You have probably decided that if the graphs of $y = x^2$ and $y = ax^2 + bx + c$ intersect at three points then $a = 1$, and $b = c = 0$. In other words, the two graphs are not distinct, but coincide everywhere.

This result can be generalised to give the following theorem.

THEOREM

If $P(x)$ and $Q(x)$ are polynomials of the same degree, n, such that $P(x) = Q(x)$ for more than n distinct values of x then $P(x) \equiv Q(x)$.

PROOF

Let $D(x) \equiv P(x) - Q(x)$.
Then $D(x) = 0 \Leftrightarrow P(x) = Q(x)$.

So $D(x)$ is a polynomial such that $D(x) = 0$ for more than n distinct values of x. That is: $D(x)$ has more than n distinct roots which implies that $D(x)$ cannot be a polynomial of degree n or less. The only possibility left is that $D(x) \equiv 0$

$$\Rightarrow P(x) - Q(x) \equiv 0$$
$$\Rightarrow P(x) \equiv Q(x).$$

Notice that since $P(x) - Q(x) \equiv 0$ all the coefficients of $P(x) - Q(x)$ are 0, so the coefficients of $P(x)$ equal the corresponding coefficients of $Q(x)$. This leads to the process which is known as *equating coefficients*.

For example: if $ax^3 + bx^2 - 5 \equiv p + qx + 6x^2 - 7x^3$
then equating coefficients gives $a = -7$, $b = 6$, $p = -5$, $q = 0$.

The results obtained so far are general: they do not depend on the type of number in use. However when you deal with particular polynomials it can be important to know whether there are any restrictions on the numbers permitted.

Thus, working with rational numbers: $x^2 - 2$ has no factors;

working with real numbers: $x^2 - 2 \equiv (x - \sqrt{2})(x + \sqrt{2}).$

Similarly, with real numbers: $x^2 - 6x + 13$ has no factors;

with complex numbers: $x^2 - 6x + 13 \equiv (x - 3 - 2j)(x - 3 + 2j).$

EXAMPLE 1.4   Find, if possible, constants p, q, r

   (i)   such that $n^2 \equiv pn(n + 2) + q(n + 1) + r(n + 2)$
   (ii)   such that $n^2 \equiv pn(n + 2) + q(n + 1)^2 + r$.

SOLUTION

   (i)   Equating coefficients: n^2: $p = 1$
                                                                 n^1: $2p + q + r = 0$
                                                                 n^0: $q + 2r = 0$

   These equations have the unique solution: $p = 1$, $q = -4$, $r = 2$.

   (ii)   Equating coefficients: n^2: $p + q = 1$
                                                                 n^1: $2p + 2q = 0$
                                                                 n^0: $q + r = 0$

   The first two equations are inconsistent, so no such p, q, r can be found.

EXAMPLE 1.5   Prove that if a, b, c are distinct, then

$$P(x) \equiv \frac{(x - a)(x - b)}{(c - a)(c - b)} + \frac{(x - b)(x - c)}{(a - b)(a - c)} + \frac{(x - c)(x - a)}{(b - c)(b - a)} - 1 \equiv 0.$$

SOLUTION

$$P(a) = 0 + \frac{(a - b)(a - c)}{(a - b)(a - c)} + 0 - 1 = 0.$$

Similarly $P(b) = P(c) = 0$.

$P(x)$ vanishes for three distinct values of x

$\Rightarrow$ $P(x)$ cannot be a polynomial of degree less than 3.

By inspection $P(x)$ is of degree no more than 2.

Therefore the degree of $P(x)$ is undefined. i.e. $P(x) \equiv 0$.

EXERCISE 1C   **1** Find constants a, b and c so that $x^2 \equiv a(x - 2)^2 + b(x - 2) + c$.

   2 Find constants a, b, c and d so that $x^3 \equiv a(x + 1)^3 + b(x + 1)^2 + c(x + 1) + d$.

   3 If $(a + b + c)x^2 + (b - c)x + (c - 2) \equiv 0$ find the values of a, b and c.

   4 Show that there are no values of the constants a and b such that

   $$x^2 \equiv ax(x + 1) + b(x + 1)(x + 2).$$

   5 What can you say about the constants a, b and c in each of the following cases?

   (i) $x \equiv a(x - 1) + b(x - 2) + c(x - 3)$
   (ii) $x^2 \equiv a(x - 1)^2 + b(x - 2)^2 + c(x - 3)^2$
   (iii) $x^3 \equiv a(x - 1)^3 + b(x - 2)^3 + c(x - 3)^3$

6 Find constants a, b and c such that $(ar + 1)^3 - (br - 1)^3 = 24r^2 + c$.

Hence show that $\sum_{r=1}^{n} r^2 = \frac{1}{6}n(n + 1)(2n + 1)$.

7 (i) Show that the equation of a straight line through (a, A), (b, B) can be written in the form

$$y = \frac{A(x - b)}{(a - b)} + \frac{B(x - a)}{(b - a)}, \quad \text{provided } a \neq b.$$

(ii) Show that the equation of the one and only quadratic curve through (a, A), (b, B) (c, C) is

$$y = \frac{A(x - b)(x - c)}{(a - b)(a - c)} + \frac{B(x - c)(x - a)}{(b - c)(b - a)} + \frac{C(x - a)(x - b)}{(c - a)(c - b)},$$

provided a, b and c are distinct.

(iii) Write down the equation of the unique cubic curve which goes through (a, A), (b, B) (C, c) and (D, d) where a, b, c and d are distinct.
(This method is due to Joseph-Louis Lagrange, 1736–1813.)

8 Use the results of Question 7 to find

(i) the equation of the quadratic curve through $(1, 1)$, $(2, 5)$, $(3, 15)$
(ii) the cubic polynomial $P(x)$ such that $P(-1) = -5$, $P(1) = 1$, $P(2) = 1$, $P(3) = 7$.

9 A quadratic approximation for 2^x is required in the interval $1 \leqslant x \leqslant 5$. By considering $h(x) = A(x - 3)(x - 5) + B(x - 1)(x - 5) + C(x - 1)(x - 3)$ where A, B and C are constants, or otherwise, find the quadratic function $h(x)$ such that $h(x) = 2^x$ when $x = 1, 3, 5$. Give your answer in the form $h(x) = ax^2 + bx + c$.

[MEI]

10 Prove that $\dfrac{a(x - b)(x - c)}{(a - b)(a - c)} + \dfrac{b(x - c)(x - a)}{(b - c)(b - a)} + \dfrac{c(x - a)(x - b)}{(c - a)(c - b)} \equiv x$,

provided a, b and c are distinct.

11 Prove that $\dfrac{a^2 - x^2}{(a - b)(a - c)} + \dfrac{b^2 - x^2}{(b - c)(b - a)} + \dfrac{c^2 - x^2}{(c - a)(c - b)} \equiv 1$,

provided a, b and c are distinct.

Repeated roots

? Figure 1.3 shows the graph of $y = f(x)$.

What can you say about the roots of the two equations

$$f(x) = 0$$
$$f'(x) = 0?$$

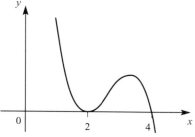

Figure 1.3

Having a little extra information often eases the problem when solving an equation, as illustrated in the next example.

EXAMPLE 1.6

Solve the equation $x^3 + x^2 - 33x + 63 = 0$ given that it has repeated roots.

SOLUTION

Let $f(x) \equiv x^3 + x^2 - 33x + 63$.

Then $f'(x) \equiv 3x^2 + 2x - 33 \equiv (3x + 11)(x - 3)$.

Since $f(x) = 0$ has a repeated root, $f(x) = 0$ and $f'(x) = 0$ have a common root.

The roots of $f'(x) = 0$ are $x = 3$ and $x = -\frac{11}{3}$;

$$f(3) = 3^3 + 3^2 - 33 \times 3 + 63 = 27 + 9 - 99 + 63 = 0 \text{ so } x = 3 \text{ is a root of } f(x) = 0.$$

As $f(x)$ is a cubic only one of the roots of $f'(x) = 0$ can also satisfy $f(x) = 0$, so you do not need to evaluate $f\left(-\frac{11}{3}\right)$.

Now $x^3 + x^2 - 33x + 63 = 0$

$\Leftrightarrow (x - 3)^2(x + 7) = 0$

> Since $x = 3$ is a repeated root, $(x - 3)$ is a repeated factor. Observe that $\frac{63}{(-3)^2} = 7$ gives the second term in final factor.

so that the roots are $x = 3$ (repeated) and $x = -7$.

EXERCISE 1D

In questions 1–7, the equations have repeated roots. Use that fact to help you solve them.

1 $x^3 - 10x^2 + 32x - 32 = 0$

2 $x^3 - 15x^2 + 72x - 108 = 0$

3 $2x^3 + 11x^2 + 12x - 9 = 0$

4 $9x^3 + 39x^2 - 29x + 5 = 0$

5 $4x^3 - 27x - 27 = 0$

6 $x^4 + x^3 - 3x^2 - 5x - 2 = 0$

7 $x^4 + 6x^3 + 13x^2 + 12x + 4 = 0$

8 Use calculus to prove that:

$$f(x) \equiv (x - a)^2 g(x) \Rightarrow f'(x) \text{ has a factor } (x - a).$$

What happens if $f(x) \equiv (x - a)^n g(x)$?

Properties of the roots of polynomial equations

Quadratic equations

In the work which follows z is used as the variable (or unknown) instead of x to emphasise that these results apply regardless of whether the roots are complex or real.

Suppose that α and β are the roots of the quadratic equations $az^2 + bz + c = 0$, $a \neq 0$. Then by the theorem proved on page 9

$$az^2 + bz + c \equiv a(z - \alpha)(z - \beta) \equiv az^2 - a(\alpha + \beta)z + a\alpha\beta.$$

Equating coefficients shows that

$$\text{the sum of the roots} = \alpha + \beta = -\frac{b}{a}$$

and the product of the roots $= \alpha\beta = \frac{c}{a}$.

From these results you can obtain information about the roots without actually solving the equation.

EXAMPLE 1.7

The roots of the equation $2z^2 + 3z + 8 = 0$ are α and β. Find

(i) the sum and product of α and β

(ii) the quadratic equation with roots α^2 and β^2.

SOLUTION

(i) $\alpha + \beta = -\frac{3}{2}$. ← sum of roots $= -\frac{b}{a}$

$\alpha\beta = \frac{8}{2} = 4$. ← product of roots $= \frac{c}{a}$

(ii) *Method 1*

$$(\alpha + \beta)^2 = \alpha^2 + \beta^2 + 2\alpha\beta \implies \left(-\frac{3}{2}\right)^2 = \alpha^2 + \beta^2 + 2 \times 4$$

$$\implies \alpha^2 + \beta^2 = \frac{9}{4} - 8 = -\frac{23}{4}.$$

$$\alpha^2\beta^2 = (\alpha\beta)^2 = 16.$$

The required equation is $z^2 - (\alpha^2 + \beta^2)z + \alpha^2\beta^2 = 0$ — sum of roots

i.e. $z^2 - \left(-\frac{23}{4}\right)z + 16 = 0$ — product of roots

which is perhaps better written as $4z^2 + 23z + 64 = 0$.

Method 2

Here is an alternative way of finding $\alpha^2 + \beta^2$.

α is root of $2z^2 + 3z + 8 = 0 \implies 2\alpha^2 + 3\alpha + 8 = 0$.
β is root of $2z^2 + 3z + 8 = 0 \implies 2\beta^2 + 3\beta + 8 = 0$.

Adding: $2(\alpha^2 + \beta^2) + 3(\alpha + \beta) + 16 = 0$

$$\implies 2(\alpha^2 + \beta^2) = -3(\alpha + \beta) - 16 = \frac{9}{2} - 16 = -\frac{23}{2}$$

$$\implies \alpha^2 + \beta^2 = -\frac{23}{4}, \text{ and then proceed as above.}$$

What happens if you try to solve the quadratic equation $az^2 + bz + c = 0$ by solving the equations $\alpha + \beta = -\frac{b}{a}$, $\alpha\beta = \frac{c}{a}$ simultaneously?

1 Write down the sum and product of the roots of each of these quadratic equations.

   (i) $2z^2 + 7z + 6 = 0$ **(ii)** $5z^2 - z - 1 = 0$
   (iii) $7z^2 + 2 = 0$ **(iv)** $5z^2 + 24z = 0$
   (v) $z(z + 8) = 4 - 3z$ **(vi)** $3z^2 + 8z - 6 = 0$

2 Write down quadratic equations (with integer coefficients) with the following roots.

   (i)   7, 3   **(ii)**   −5, −4.5
   (iii) 5, 0   **(iv)**   3 repeated
   (v) $3 - 2j$, $3 + 2j$

3 The roots of $z^2 - 2z + 3 = 0$ are α and β.

   (i)   Write down the values of $\alpha + \beta$ and $\alpha\beta$ and deduce the values of $\frac{1}{\alpha} + \frac{1}{\beta}$ and $\frac{1}{\alpha} \times \frac{1}{\beta}$.

   (ii)   Write down the equation (with integer coefficients) whose roots are $\frac{1}{\alpha}$, $\frac{1}{\beta}$.

   (iii) Find the equation whose roots are the reciprocals of the roots of $az^2 + bz + c = 0$.

4 The roots of $2z^2 + 5z - 9 = 0$ are α and β. Find quadratic equations with roots

   (i) $-\alpha$ and $-\beta$ **(ii)** $2\alpha + \beta$ and $\alpha + 2\beta$
   (iii) α^2 and β^2 **(iv)** $\frac{\alpha}{\beta}$ and $\frac{\beta}{\alpha}$.

5 The roots of the equation $z^2 + 8z - 2 = 0$ are α and β. Find the equation with roots $\alpha^2\beta$ and $\alpha\beta^2$.

6 The roots of $az^2 + bz + c = 0$ are α and β. Find quadratic equations with roots

   (i) $k\alpha$ and $k\beta$
   (ii) $k + \alpha$ and $k + \beta$.

7 Using the fact that $\alpha + \beta = -\frac{b}{a}$, $\alpha\beta = \frac{c}{a}$, what can you say about the roots α and β of $az^2 + bz + c = 0$ if you also know that

   (i) a, b, c are all positive and $b^2 - 4ac > 0$
   (ii) $b = 0$
   (iii) $c = 0$
   (iv) a and c have opposite signs?

8 One root of $az^2 + bz + c = 0$ is twice the other. Prove that $2b^2 = 9ac$.

9 (i) The straight line $y = 2x + k$ meets the parabola $y = 3x^2 - 4x - 11$ at the points P and Q. Form a quadratic equation for the x co-ordinates of P and Q. Without solving this equation find the x co-ordinate of M, the mid-point of PQ. What do you deduce about the locus of M as k varies?

(ii) By considering the locus of the mid-point of chords of fixed gradient m, generalise this result to the parabola $y = ax^2 + bx + c$.

Cubic equations

There are corresponding properties for the roots of cubic and quartic equations (as well as equations of higher degree). If α, β, γ are the roots of the cubic equation $az^3 + bz^2 + cz + d = 0$ then, as before,

$$az^3 + bz^2 + cz + d \equiv a(z - \alpha)(z - \beta)(z - \gamma)$$
$$\equiv az^3 - a(\alpha + \beta + \gamma)z^2 + a(\alpha\beta + \beta\gamma + \gamma\alpha)z - a\alpha\beta\gamma.$$

Equating coefficients gives these results for roots of cubic equations:

$$\alpha + \beta + \gamma = -\frac{b}{a},$$ *sum of individual roots*

$$\alpha\beta + \beta\gamma + \gamma\alpha = \frac{c}{a},$$ *sum of products of roots in pairs*

$$\alpha\beta\gamma = -\frac{d}{a}.$$ *product of roots*

As with the roots of quadratic equations, you cannot find the roots directly from these equations because attempting to solve them simultaneously merely leads you back to the original cubic equation (with α or β or γ in place of z). But if you have additional information these equations can provide a quick and easy method of solution.

Note

For brevity $\Sigma\alpha$ and $\Sigma\alpha\beta$ are often used to denote $\alpha + \beta + \gamma$ and $\alpha\beta + \beta\gamma + \gamma\alpha$ respectively. There is no ambiguity, provided you know the degree of the relevant equation. Funtions like these are called symmetric functions of the roots, because interchange of any two of α, β, γ leaves their value unchanged. Similar notation is used to denote other symmetric functions of the roots. For example: the sum of all products of one root with the square of another

$$= \Sigma\alpha^2\beta = \alpha^2\beta + \alpha\beta^2 + \alpha^2\gamma + \alpha\gamma^2 + \beta^2\gamma + \beta\gamma^2.$$

The following identities are often useful.

(i) $(\sum \alpha)^2 \equiv \sum \alpha^2 + 2\sum \alpha\beta$

(ii) $\alpha\beta\gamma\sum\alpha^{-1} \equiv \sum\alpha\beta$

(iii) $\sum\alpha^3 - 3\alpha\beta\gamma \equiv (\sum\alpha)(\sum\alpha^2 - \sum\alpha\beta)$

I ACTIVITY

Write the above identities out in full, and prove them.

EXAMPLE 1.7

Solve the equation $2z^3 - 9z^2 - 27z + 54 = 0$ given that the roots form a geometric progression.

SOLUTION

Let the three roots be $\frac{\alpha}{r}$, α, αr.

> You could use α, αr, αr^2 but this choice makes for simpler equations as the product of the three roots does not contain r.

The product of the roots $= \alpha^3 = -\frac{54}{2} = -27 \Leftrightarrow \alpha = -3$.

The sum of the roots $= \sum\alpha = \frac{\alpha}{r} + \alpha + \alpha r = \frac{9}{2}$

$\Leftrightarrow 2r^2 + 5r + 2 = 0$

> Substituting for α, multiplying by $\frac{2r}{3}$ and rearranging.

$\Leftrightarrow (2r + 1)(r + 2) = 0$

$\Leftrightarrow r = -2$ or $r = -\frac{1}{2}$.

Both values of r tell you that the three roots are $\frac{3}{2}$, -3, 6.

EXAMPLE 1.8

The roots of the cubic equation $az^3 + bz^2 + cz + d = 0$ are α, β, γ, where $\alpha\beta\gamma \neq 0$. Find the cubic equation with roots $\frac{1}{\alpha}$, $\frac{1}{\beta}$, $\frac{1}{\gamma}$.

SOLUTION

Method 1

$\frac{1}{\alpha} + \frac{1}{\beta} + \frac{1}{\gamma} = \frac{\beta\gamma + \gamma\alpha + \alpha\beta}{\alpha\beta\gamma} = \frac{c/a}{-d/a} = -\frac{c}{d}$.

$\frac{1}{\alpha} \times \frac{1}{\beta} + \frac{1}{\beta} \times \frac{1}{\gamma} + \frac{1}{\gamma} \times \frac{1}{\alpha} = \frac{\gamma + \alpha + \beta}{\alpha\beta\gamma} = \frac{-b/a}{-d/a} = \frac{b}{d}$.

$\frac{1}{\alpha} \times \frac{1}{\beta} \times \frac{1}{\gamma} = \frac{1}{\alpha\beta\gamma} = -\frac{a}{d}$.

So the required equation is

$$z^3 - \left(-\frac{c}{d}\right)z^2 + \frac{b}{d}z - \left(-\frac{a}{d}\right) = 0 \Leftrightarrow dz^3 + cz^2 + bz + a = 0.$$

Method 2 (by substitution)

Let $w = \frac{1}{z}$ so that $z = \frac{1}{w}$. Then

α, β, γ are the roots of $az^3 + bz^2 + cz + d = 0$ if and only if

$\frac{1}{\alpha}$, $\frac{1}{\beta}$, $\frac{1}{\gamma}$ are the roots of $a \times \frac{1}{w^3} + b \times \frac{1}{w^2} + c \times \frac{1}{w} + d = 0$

$\Leftrightarrow a + bw + cw^2 + dw^3 = 0$.

Notice that taking the reciprocal of each root reverses the coefficients of the equation. This property applies to polynomial equations of all degrees, provided that none of the roots is zero.

The substitution method used above (Method 2) is powerful. It is used again in the next example.

EXAMPLE 1.9

The roots of the cubic equation $az^3 + bz^2 + cz + d = 0$ are α, β, γ. Find the cubic equation with roots **(i)** $3\alpha + 7$, $3\beta + 7$, $3\gamma + 7$ **(ii)** α^2, β^2, γ^2.

SOLUTION

(i) Let $w = 3z + 7$ so that $z = \dfrac{w - 7}{3}$. Then α, β, γ are the roots of $az^3 + bz^2 + cz + d = 0$ if and only if $3\alpha + 7$, $3\beta + 7$, $3\gamma + 7$

are the roots of $a\left(\dfrac{w-7}{3}\right)^3 + b\left(\dfrac{w-7}{3}\right)^2 + c\left(\dfrac{w-7}{3}\right) + d = 0$

$$\Leftrightarrow a(w^3 - 21w^2 + 147w - 343) + 3b(w^2 - 14w + 49) + 9c(w - 7) + 27d = 0$$

which simplifies to

$$aw^3 - 3(7a - b)w^2 + 3(49a - 14b + 3c)w - (343a - 147b + 63c - 27d) = 0.$$

(ii) Let $w = z^2$. Then

$$az^3 + bz^2 + cz + d = 0 \Rightarrow awz + bw + cz + d = 0$$
$$\Rightarrow (aw + c)z = -(bw + d)$$
$$\Rightarrow (aw + c)^2 w = (bw + d)^2$$
$$\Rightarrow a^2 w^3 + (2ac - b^2)w^2 + (c^2 - 2bd)w - d^2 = 0.$$

> Substituting w for z^2 wherever it occurs.

> Squaring and then substituting w for z^2 again, to get rid of z.

ACTIVITY

The cubic equation $az^3 + bz^2 + cz + d = 0$ has roots α, β, γ. Explain why substituting $-\dfrac{d}{aw}$ for z in $az^3 + bz^2 + cz + d = 0$ forms an equation with roots $\alpha\beta$, $\beta\gamma$, $\gamma\alpha$. Simplify the resulting equation as much as possible and show that your result is valid even if one of α, β, γ is zero.

EXERCISE 1F

1 The roots of $2z^3 + 3z^2 - z + 7 = 0$ are α, β, γ. Find

(i) $\sum \alpha$

(ii) $\sum \alpha\beta$

(iii) $\alpha\beta\gamma$

(iv) $\sum \alpha^2$

(v) $\sum \alpha^3$

(vi) $\sum \alpha^4$

(vii) $\sum \dfrac{1}{\alpha}$

(viii) $\sum \dfrac{1}{\alpha\beta}$

(ix) $\sum \alpha^2\beta$

(x) $\sum \dfrac{\alpha + \beta}{\gamma}$.

2 The roots of $z^3 - 4z^2 - z + 3 = 0$ are α, β, γ. Find cubic equations whose roots are

(i) 2α, 2β, 2γ

(ii) $\alpha + 2$, $\beta + 2$, $\gamma + 2$

(iii) $\alpha + \beta$, $\beta + \gamma$, $\gamma + \alpha$.

3 Solve these equations given that the roots are in arithmetic progression.

    (i) $z^3 - 15z^2 + 66z - 80 = 0$

    (ii) $9z^3 - 18z^2 - 4z + 8 = 0$

    (iii) $z^3 - 6z^2 + 16 = 0$

    (iv) $54z^3 - 189z^2 + 207z - 70 = 0$

4 The roots of the equation $2z^3 - 12z^2 + kz - 15 = 0$ are in arithmetic progression. Solve the equation and find k.

5 Solve $32z^3 - 14z + 3 = 0$, given that one root is twice another.

6 The roots of $az^3 + bz^2 + cz + d = 0$ are α, β, γ. Form cubic equations with roots

    (i) $\alpha^2, \beta^2, \gamma^2$

    (ii) $\dfrac{1}{\alpha^2}, \dfrac{1}{\beta^2}, \dfrac{1}{\gamma^2}$

    (iii) $\dfrac{\beta\gamma}{\alpha}, \dfrac{\gamma\alpha}{\beta}, \dfrac{\alpha\beta}{\gamma}.$

7 Find a formula connecting a, b, c, d which is a necessary and sufficient condition for the roots of the equation $az^3 + bz^2 + cz + d = 0$ to be in geometric progression. Show that this condition is satisfied for the equation $8z^3 - 52z^2 + 78z - 27 = 0$, and hence solve the equation.

8 The roots of the cubic equation $x^3 - 5x^2 - 6x - 4 = 0$ are α, β and γ.

    (i)   Write down the values of $\alpha + \beta + \gamma$, $\alpha\beta + \beta\gamma + \gamma\alpha$ and $\alpha\beta\gamma$.

    (ii) Find the values of $\alpha^2 + \beta^2 + \gamma^2$.

    (iii) Show that $(\alpha\beta)^2 + (\beta\gamma)^2 + (\gamma\alpha)^2 = -4$. Deduce that α, β and γ are not all real.

    (iv) Find a cubic equation with integer coefficients whose roots are $\dfrac{\beta\gamma}{\alpha}, \dfrac{\gamma\alpha}{\beta}$ and $\dfrac{\alpha\beta}{\gamma}$.

                                                                             [MEI]

9 The equation $z^3 + pz^2 + 2pz + q = 0$ has roots $\alpha, 2\alpha, 4\alpha$. Find all the possible values of p, q, α.

10 Show that one root of $az^3 + bz^2 + cz + d = 0$ is the reciprocal of another root if and only if $a^2 - d^2 = ac - bd$.

    Verify that this condition is satisfied for the equation $21z^3 - 16z^2 - 95z + 42 = 0$ and hence solve the equation.

11 The roots of $z^3 + pz^2 + qz + r = 0$ are $\alpha, -\alpha, \beta$, and $r \neq 0$. Show that $r = pq$, and find all three roots in terms of p and q.

12 The cubic equation $2x^3 - 3x^2 - 12x - 4 = 0$ has roots α, β and γ.

   (i) Write down the values of $\alpha + \beta + \gamma$, $\beta\gamma + \gamma\alpha + \alpha\beta$ and $\alpha\beta\gamma$.

   (ii) Find $\alpha^2 + \beta^2 + \gamma^2$ and $(\beta\gamma)^2 + (\gamma\alpha)^2 + (\alpha\beta)^2$.

   (iii) By considering $(\alpha + \beta + \gamma)(\beta\gamma + \gamma\alpha + \alpha\beta)$, show that

$$\alpha^2\beta + \alpha^2\gamma + \beta^2\gamma + \beta^2\alpha + \gamma^2\alpha + \gamma^2\beta = -15.$$

   (iv) Find a cubic equation with integer coefficients which has roots

$$\alpha - \beta\gamma, \beta - \gamma\alpha \text{ and } \gamma - \alpha\beta.$$

[MEI]

13 The cubic equation $16x^3 + kx^2 + 27 = 0$ (where k is a real constant) has roots α, β and γ.

   (i) Write down the values of $\beta\gamma + \gamma\alpha + \alpha\beta$ and $\alpha\beta\gamma$, and express k in terms of α, β and γ.

   (ii) For the case where there is a repeated root, say $\beta = \gamma$, solve the cubic equation, and find the value of k.

   (iii) For the case $k = 9$, find a cubic equation with integer coefficients which has roots

$$\frac{1}{\alpha} + 1, \frac{1}{\beta} + 1, \frac{1}{\gamma} + 1.$$

[MEI]

Quartic equations

Similar methods can be used to treat the roots of quartic equations. If α, β, γ, δ are the roots of $az^4 + bz^3 + cz^2 + dz + e = 0$, where $a \neq 0$, then

$$
\begin{aligned}
az^4 + bz^3 + cz^2 + dz + e &\equiv a(z - \alpha)(z - \beta)(z - \gamma)(z - \delta) \\
&\equiv az^4 - a(\alpha + \beta + \gamma + \delta)z^3 + a(\alpha\beta + \alpha\gamma + \alpha\delta + \beta\gamma + \beta\delta + \gamma\delta)z^2 \\
&\quad - a(\alpha\beta\gamma + \beta\gamma\delta + \gamma\delta\alpha + \delta\alpha\beta)z + a\alpha\beta\gamma\delta.
\end{aligned}
$$

Equating coefficients shows that:

$$\Sigma\alpha = \alpha + \beta + \gamma + \delta = -\frac{b}{a},$$ (sum of individual roots)

$$\Sigma\alpha\beta = \alpha\beta + \alpha\gamma + \alpha\delta + \beta\gamma + \beta\delta + \gamma\delta = \frac{c}{a},$$ (sum of products of roots in pairs)

$$\Sigma\alpha\beta\gamma = \alpha\beta\gamma + \beta\gamma\delta + \gamma\delta\alpha + \delta\alpha\beta = -\frac{d}{a},$$ (sum of products of roots in threes)

$$\alpha\beta\gamma\delta = \frac{e}{a}.$$ (product of roots)

EXAMPLE 1.10

The roots of the quartic equation $z^4 + 3z^3 - 2z^2 - z + 5 = 0$ are $\alpha, \beta, \gamma, \delta$. Find $\sum \alpha^3$.

SOLUTION

$\alpha\beta\gamma\delta = 5 \Rightarrow$ none of $\alpha, \beta, \gamma, \delta$ is zero.

$\sum \alpha = -\dfrac{b}{a} = -3.$

$\sum \alpha\beta = -\dfrac{c}{a} = -2.$

α is a root $\Rightarrow \alpha^4 + 3\alpha^3 - 2\alpha^2 - \alpha + 5 = 0 \Rightarrow \alpha^3 + 3\alpha^2 - 2\alpha - 1 + 5\alpha^{-1} = 0$

$\qquad\qquad\qquad\qquad\qquad\qquad\qquad\qquad \Rightarrow \alpha^3 = -3\alpha^2 + 2\alpha + 1 - 5\alpha^{-1}$

with similar expressions for $\beta^3, \gamma^3, \delta^3$. Adding these four expressions gives

$$\sum \alpha^3 = -3\sum \alpha^2 + 2\sum \alpha + 4 - 5\sum \alpha^{-1}$$

You are adding four expressions.

$$= -3[(\sum \alpha)^2 - 2\sum \alpha\beta] + 2\sum \alpha + 4 - 5\sum \alpha^{-1}$$

$\sum \alpha^2 \equiv (\sum \alpha)^2 - 2\sum \alpha\beta$

$$= -3[(-3)^2 - 2(-2)] + 2(-3) + 4 - 5 \times \tfrac{1}{5}$$

$$= -42.$$

$\sum \alpha^{-1} = -\dfrac{d}{e} = \dfrac{1}{5}$ since taking the reciprocals of the roots reverses the coefficients of the equation.

1 The roots of $2z^4 + 3z^3 + 6z^2 - 5z + 4 = 0$ are $\alpha, \beta, \gamma, \delta$. Find

(i) $\sum \alpha^2$ (ii) $\sum (\alpha + \beta + \gamma)^2$

(iii) $\sum \alpha\beta^2$ (iv) $\sum (\alpha + \beta)^3$.

2 Prove the following identities for quartics.

(i) $(\sum \alpha)^2 \equiv \sum \alpha^2 + 2\sum \alpha\beta$

(ii) $\alpha\beta\gamma\delta \sum \alpha^{-1} \equiv \sum \alpha\beta\gamma$

(iii) $\sum \alpha^3 - 3\sum \alpha\beta\gamma \equiv (\sum \alpha)(\sum \alpha^2 - \sum \alpha\beta)$

3 The roots of the quartic equation $x^4 + 8x^3 + 20x^2 + 16x + 4 = 0$ are α, β, γ and δ.

(i) Find the values of

  (a) $\alpha + \beta + \gamma + \delta$

  (b) $\alpha^2 + \beta^2 + \gamma^2 + \delta^2$

  (c) $\dfrac{1}{\alpha} + \dfrac{1}{\beta} + \dfrac{1}{\gamma} + \dfrac{1}{\delta}$

  (d) $\dfrac{\alpha}{\beta\gamma\delta} + \dfrac{\beta}{\alpha\gamma\delta} + \dfrac{\gamma}{\alpha\beta\delta} + \dfrac{\delta}{\alpha\beta\gamma}$.

(ii) By making a suitable substitution, find a quartic equation with roots

$$\alpha + 2, \beta + 2, \gamma + 2 \text{ and } \delta + 2.$$

(iii) Solve the equation found in **(ii)**, and hence find the values of α, β, γ and δ.

[MEI]

4 The roots of $z^4 + pz^3 + qz^2 + rz + s = 0$ are $\alpha, \beta, \gamma, \delta$.

Prove that $\alpha\beta = \gamma\delta \implies s = \dfrac{r^2}{p^2}$.

5 The quartic equation $9x^4 + px^3 - 32x + q = 0$, where p and q are real, has roots $\alpha, 3\alpha, \beta, -\beta$.

(i) By considering the coefficients of x^2 and x, find α and β, where $\beta > 0$.

(ii) Show that $p = 24$, and find the value of q.

(iii) By making the substitution $y = x - k$, for a suitable value of k, find a cubic equation with integer coefficients which has roots $-2\alpha, \beta - 3\alpha, -\beta - 3\alpha$.

[MEI]

6 The quartic equation $3x^4 - 9x^2 - 6x - 2 = 0$ has roots α, β, γ and δ.

(i) Find the values of

(a) $\alpha + \beta + \gamma + \delta$

(b) $\alpha\beta\gamma\delta$

(c) $\alpha^2 + \beta^2 + \gamma^2 + \delta^2$

(d) $\dfrac{1}{\alpha} + \dfrac{1}{\beta} + \dfrac{1}{\gamma} + \dfrac{1}{\delta}$.

(ii) Using the substitution $y = \dfrac{1}{x^2}$, or otherwise, find a quartic equation with integer coefficients which has roots $\dfrac{1}{\alpha^2}, \dfrac{1}{\beta^2}, \dfrac{1}{\gamma^2}$ and $\dfrac{1}{\delta^2}$.

(iii) Find the value of $\dfrac{1}{\alpha^2} + \dfrac{1}{\beta^2} + \dfrac{1}{\gamma^2} + \dfrac{1}{\delta^2}$.

Comment on the nature of the roots α, β, γ and δ.

[MEI]

7 The equation $x^4 - 6x^3 - 73x^2 + kx + m = 0$ has two positive roots α, β and two negative roots γ, δ. It is given that $\alpha\beta = \gamma\delta = 4$.

(i) Find the values of the constants k and m.

(ii) Show that $(\alpha + \beta)(\gamma + \delta) = -81$.

(iii) Find the quadratic equation which has roots $\alpha + \beta, \gamma + \delta$.

(iv) Find $\alpha + \beta$ and $\gamma + \delta$.

(v) Show that $\alpha^2 - 3(1 + \sqrt{10})\alpha + 4 = 0$, and find similar quadratic equations satisfied by β, γ and δ.

[MEI]

INVESTIGATION

Investigate the following iterative procedure for solving the quadratic equation $ax^2 + bx + c = 0$: first choose a starting value (α_0); then use $\alpha_n + \beta_n = -\dfrac{b}{a}$ and $\alpha_{n+1}\beta_n = \dfrac{c}{a}$ to find β_0 and other values of α_n and β_n.

1 The remainder theorem:

If the polynomial $P(x)$ is divided by $x - a$ the remainder is $P(a)$.

2 A polynomial of degree n cannot take the value zero for more than n distinct values of x.

3 If $P(x)$ and $Q(x)$ are polynomials of the same degree, n, such that $P(x) = Q(x)$ for more than n distinct values of x, then $P(x) \equiv Q(x)$.

4 If α and β are the roots of the quadratic equation $az^2 + bz + c = 0$, then

$$\alpha + \beta = -\frac{b}{a},$$
$$\alpha\beta = \frac{c}{a}.$$

5 If α, β, γ are the roots of the cubic equation $az^3 + bz^2 + cz + d = 0$, then

$$\sum \alpha = \alpha + \beta + \gamma = -\frac{b}{a},$$
$$\sum \alpha\beta = \alpha\beta + \beta\gamma + \gamma\alpha = \frac{c}{a},$$
$$\alpha\beta\gamma = -\frac{d}{a}.$$

6 If $\alpha, \beta, \gamma, \delta$ are the roots of the quartic equation $az^4 + bz^3 + cz^2 + dz + e = 0$, then

$$\sum \alpha = \alpha + \beta + \gamma + \delta = -\frac{b}{a},$$
$$\sum \alpha\beta = \alpha\beta + \alpha\gamma + \alpha\delta + \beta\gamma + \beta\delta + \gamma\delta = \frac{c}{a},$$
$$\sum \alpha\beta\gamma = \alpha\beta\gamma + \beta\gamma\delta + \gamma\delta\alpha + \delta\alpha\beta = -\frac{d}{a},$$
$$\alpha\beta\gamma\delta = \frac{e}{a}.$$

2

2

Geometry with polar co-ordinates

This Nautilus shell forms an equiangular spiral. How could you describe this mathematically?

Polar co-ordinates

When dealing with the polar form of a complex number (*Pure Mathematics 4,* page 30) you used the idea of describing the position of a point P in a plane by giving its distance r from a fixed point O and the angle θ between OP and a fixed direction. In this system, first used by Newton in 1671, O is called the *pole* and the angle θ is measured from the initial line, which is usually drawn to the right across the page, like the positive x axis; the numbers (r, θ) are called the *polar co-ordinates* of P; see figure 2.1.

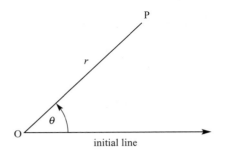

Figure 2.1

As before, the angle θ is positive in the anticlockwise sense from the initial line; at the pole itself $r = 0$ and θ is undefined. Each pair of numbers (r, θ) gives a unique point, but the converse is not true, for two reasons. Firstly, a point is not changed if you add any integer multiple of 2π to the angle θ. Secondly, it is sometimes convenient to let r take negative values (something which does not happen with complex numbers since $|z| \geqslant 0$), with the natural interpretation that the point $(-r, \theta)$ is the same as $(r, \theta + \pi)$.

ACTIVITY

Check by drawing a diagram that the polar co-ordinates

$\left(5, \frac{\pi}{3}\right), \left(5, \frac{7\pi}{3}\right), \left(5, -\frac{11\pi}{3}\right)$ and $\left(-5, -\frac{2\pi}{3}\right)$ all describe the same point.

Give three other pairs of polar co-ordinates for the point $\left(-6, \frac{3\pi}{4}\right)$.

If it is necessary to specify the polar co-ordinates of a point uniquely then you use those for which $r > 0$ and $-\pi < \theta \leqslant \pi$; these are called the *principal polar co-ordinates*.

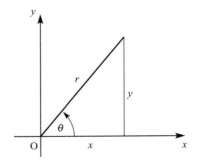

Figure 2.2

It is easy to change between polar co-ordinates (r, θ) and cartesian co-ordinates (x, y) since, from figure 2.2,

$$x = r\cos\theta \qquad y = r\sin\theta \qquad r = \sqrt{x^2 + y^2} \qquad \tan\theta = \frac{y}{x}$$

You need to be careful to choose the right quadrant when finding θ, since the equation $\tan\theta = \frac{y}{x}$ always gives two solutions, differing by π. Always draw a sketch to check which one of these is correct.

EXERCISE 2A

1 Plot the points A, B, C, D with polar co-ordinates $\left(3, \frac{\pi}{5}\right), \left(2, \frac{7\pi}{10}\right), \left(3, -\frac{4\pi}{5}\right), \left(-4, \frac{7\pi}{10}\right)$ respectively. What shape is ABCD?

2 One vertex of an equilateral triangle has polar co-ordinates $\left(4, \frac{\pi}{4}\right)$. Find the polar co-ordinates of all the possible other vertices

   (i)   when the origin O is the centre of the triangle

   (ii)   when O is another vertex of the triangle

   (iii)   when O is the mid-point of one side of the triangle.

3 The diagram shows a regular pentagon OABCD, in which A has cartesian co-ordinates (5, 2).

   (i)   Show that OB = 8.71 (correct to 2 decimal places).

   (ii)   Find the polar co-ordinates of A, B, C, D.

   (iii)   Hence find the cartesian co-ordinates of B, C, D.

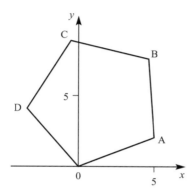

[In **(ii)** and **(iii)** give your answers correct to 2 decimal places.]

4 In this question r is in millimetres and θ is in degrees. The scoring region of a dartboard is marked by six concentric circles, called inner bull, outer bull, inner treble, outer treble, inner double, outer double, with radii 6, 16, 99, 107, 162, 170 mm respectively (to the nearest mm, ignoring the thickness of the dividing wire). The part between the outer bull and outer double circles is divided into twenty equal 'sectors', numbered as shown below, and the board is hung with the 20 sector vertically above the centre so that the initial line bisects the 6 sector. A dart scores 50 in the inner bull and 25 in the outer bull, where $6 < r < 16$. A dart in a sector scores the sector number, except that within the doubles ring ($162 < r < 170$) or trebles ring ($99 < r < 107$) it scores double or treble the sector number respectively.

   (i)   Find the score in the region for which $16 < r < 99$ and $27 < \theta < 45$.

   (ii)   Give conditions on r and θ which define the boundary between sectors 10 and 15.

   (iii)   Give conditions on r and θ for the regions in which the score is

      (a) treble 14

      (b) 17

      (c) 18.

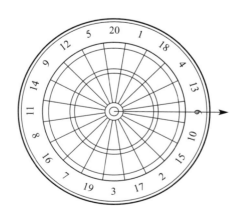

The polar equation of a curve

The points (r, θ) for which the values of r and θ are linked by a function f form a curve whose *polar equation* is $r = f(\theta)$. The polar equation of a curve may be simpler than its cartesian equation, especially if the curve has rotational symmetry. Polar equations have many important applications, for example in the study of orbits.

EXAMPLE 2.1

Investigate the curve with polar equation $r = 10\cos\theta$.

SOLUTION

This can be tackled in three ways.

(i) *By plotting.* Make a table of values. This one has θ increasing by $\dfrac{\pi}{12}$ (i.e. 15°), which gives a convenient number of points.

θ	0	$\dfrac{\pi}{12}$	$\dfrac{\pi}{6}$	$\dfrac{\pi}{4}$	$\dfrac{\pi}{3}$	$\dfrac{5\pi}{12}$	$\dfrac{\pi}{2}$	$\dfrac{7\pi}{12}$	$\dfrac{2\pi}{3}$	$\dfrac{3\pi}{4}$	$\dfrac{5\pi}{6}$	$\dfrac{11\pi}{12}$	π
r	10	9.7	8.7	7.1	5.0	2.6	0	−2.6	−5.0	−7.1	−8.7	−9.7	−10

Values of θ from 0 to $-\pi$ (or from π to 2π) give the same points again: for example, $\theta = -\dfrac{\pi}{12} \Rightarrow r = 9.7$, which is the same point as $\left(-9.7, \dfrac{11\pi}{12}\right)$. Plotting these points gives the curve shown in figure 2.3.

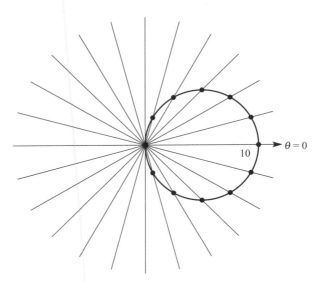

Figure 2.3

(ii) *By converting to cartesian form.* If $r \neq 0$ then

$$r = 10\cos\theta \iff r^2 = 10r\cos\theta$$
$$\iff x^2 + y^2 = 10x.$$

If $r = 0$ then $x = y = 0$, which also satisfies $x^2 + y^2 = 10x$.

Therefore the cartesian equation is $x^2 + y^2 = 10x$

$$\iff (x-5)^2 + y^2 = 25,$$

which shows that the curve is the circle with radius 5 and centre $(5, 0)$ (in cartesian co-ordinates).

(iii) *By geometrical reasoning.* Knowing the answer leads to an even simpler solution. If P is the point on this circle with polar co-ordinates (r, θ) then OPA is a right angle (the angle in a semi-circle) and so $r = 10\cos\theta$ as required, and the same applies to points on the lower semi-circle since the cosine function is an even function.

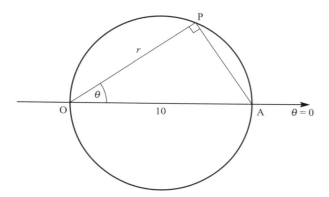

Figure 2.4

Notes

1 Plotting and joining points as in **(i)** above gives a good idea of the shape of the curve, but the argument in **(ii)** or **(iii)** is needed before you can be sure that this is truly a circle.

2 As the value of θ increases from $-\pi$ to π the point moves twice around the circle.

ACTIVITY

If you have access to a graphic calculator or a computer with suitable software, find out how to draw a curve from its polar equation. Check that you can adjust the scales so that in this case you get a circle, not just an ellipse.

❓ Some graphic calculators will not draw the curve $r = f(\theta)$ directly, but instead you can take θ as a parameter and draw the curve with parametric equations $x = f(\theta)\cos\theta$, $y = f(\theta)\sin\theta$. Explain why this works.

EXAMPLE 2.2

(i) Describe the motion of a point along the curve $r = 1 + 2\cos\theta$ as θ increases from 0 to 2π.

(ii) Do the same for the curve $r = \dfrac{1}{1 + 2\cos\theta}$.

SOLUTION

(i) The curve is shown in figure 2.5.

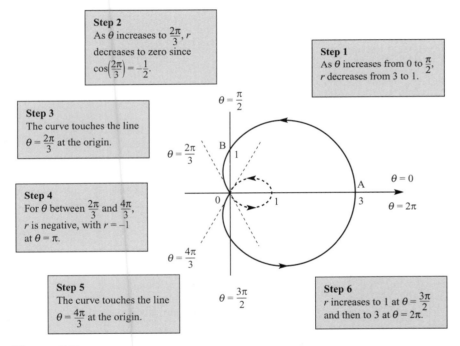

Step 2
As θ increases to $\dfrac{2\pi}{3}$, r decreases to zero since $\cos\left(\dfrac{2\pi}{3}\right) = -\dfrac{1}{2}$.

Step 1
As θ increases from 0 to $\dfrac{\pi}{2}$, r decreases from 3 to 1.

Step 3
The curve touches the line $\theta = \dfrac{2\pi}{3}$ at the origin.

Step 4
For θ between $\dfrac{2\pi}{3}$ and $\dfrac{4\pi}{3}$, r is negative, with $r = -1$ at $\theta = \pi$.

Step 5
The curve touches the line $\theta = \dfrac{4\pi}{3}$ at the origin.

Step 6
r increases to 1 at $\theta = \dfrac{3\pi}{2}$ and then to 3 at $\theta = 2\pi$.

Figure 2.5

This double loop is one of a family of curves called *limaçons* (snail curves); see the investigation on page 35.

(ii) The value of r is now the reciprocal of the value found in **(i)**; the curve is shown in figure 2.6.

This curve has two separate branches; it is an example of a hyperbola, and will be dealt with in detail later, in Chapter 5.

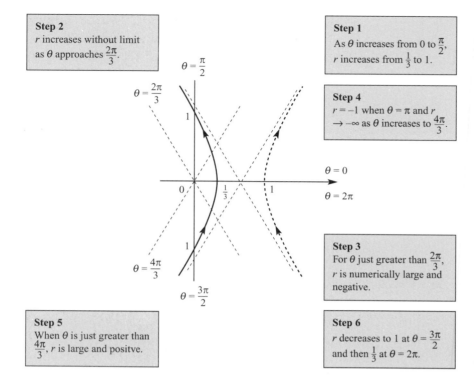

Step 2
r increases without limit as θ approaches $\frac{2\pi}{3}$.

Step 1
As θ increases from 0 to $\frac{\pi}{2}$, r increases from $\frac{1}{3}$ to 1.

Step 4
$r = -1$ when $\theta = \pi$ and $r \to -\infty$ as θ increases to $\frac{4\pi}{3}$.

Step 3
For θ just greater than $\frac{2\pi}{3}$, r is numerically large and negative.

Step 5
When θ is just greater than $\frac{4\pi}{3}$, r is large and positve.

Step 6
r decreases to 1 at $\theta = \frac{3\pi}{2}$ and then $\frac{1}{3}$ at $\theta = 2\pi$.

Figure 2.6

Note

The diagrams in the example above use the convention that the parts of the curve for which $r < 0$ are shown by a broken line. In some applications it is physically impossible for r to be negative, so it is worth distinguishing such portions in this way.

In this exercise you should make full but critical use of a graphic calculator or computer if these are available.

1 Make a table of values of $8 \sin \theta$ for θ from 0 to π at intervals of $\frac{\pi}{12}$ ($= 15°$), and say what happens when $\pi \leqslant \theta \leqslant 2\pi$. By plotting points draw the curve $r = 8 \sin \theta$. Prove that this curve is a circle, and give its cartesian equation.

2 Draw the graph of the *spiral of Archimedes*

$$r = \frac{4\theta}{\pi} \text{ for } -2\pi \leqslant \theta \leqslant 2\pi.$$

3 A curve with polar equation $r = k \sin n\theta$, where k and n are positive and n is an integer, is called a *rhodonea* (rose curve). Throughout this question take $k = 10$.

(i) What shape is the curve when $n = 1$?

(ii) Draw the curve when $n = 2$.

(iii) Draw the curve when $n = 3$.

(iv) From these examples (and others if you wish) form a conjecture about how the number of 'petals' depends on n.

4 A curve with polar equation $r = a(1 + \cos\theta)$ is called a *cardioid*. Draw the curve when $a = 8$, and account for its name.

5 Prove that $r = a\sec\theta$ and $r = b\operatorname{cosec}\theta$, where a and b are non-zero constants, are the polar equations of two straight lines. Find their cartesian equations.

6 The straight line ℓ passes through the point A with polar co-ordinates (p, α) and is perpendicular to OA. Prove that the polar equation of ℓ is $r\cos(\theta - \alpha) = p$.

Use the expansion of $\cos(\theta - \alpha)$ to find the cartesian equation of ℓ.

7 Sketch on the same diagram the curves with polar equations $r = 2a\cos\theta$, $2r(1 + \cos\theta) = 3a$ and find the polar co-ordinates of their points of intersection.

What is the polar equation of the common chord of the two curves?

[MEI]

The area of a sector

The region bounded by an arc UV of a curve and the two lines OU and OV is called a *sector*. In order to find the area of the sector for which OU and OV are the lines $\theta = \alpha$ and $\theta = \beta$ and the curve is $r = f(\theta)$ you first divide it into small sectors such as OPQ, where P and Q have co-ordinates (r, θ) and $(r + \delta r, \theta + \delta\theta)$, as in figure 2.7

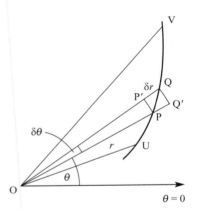

Figure 2.7

Let the areas of sectors OUP and OPQ be A and δA respectively. Then since the area of sector OPQ lies between the area of the circular sectors OPP′ and OQQ′,

$$\tfrac{1}{2}r^2\delta\theta < \delta A < \tfrac{1}{2}(r + \delta r)^2\delta\theta$$

> Remember that θ is in radians.

and so $\tfrac{1}{2}r^2 < \dfrac{\delta A}{\delta\theta} < \tfrac{1}{2}(r + \delta r)^2.$

Now as $\delta\theta \to 0$, $\dfrac{\delta A}{\delta\theta} \to \dfrac{\mathrm{d}A}{\mathrm{d}\theta}$, the rate of change of A with respect to θ.

But $\dfrac{\delta A}{\delta\theta}$ is trapped between $\frac{1}{2}r^2$, which is fixed, and $\frac{1}{2}(r+\delta r)^2$, which tends to $\frac{1}{2}r^2$, and so $\dfrac{\delta A}{\delta\theta}$ must also tend to $\frac{1}{2}r^2$. Therefore

$$\frac{\mathrm{d}A}{\mathrm{d}\theta} = \tfrac{1}{2}r^2.$$

From this key result the area of the sector can be found by integration:

$$\text{area OUV} = \int_{\alpha}^{\beta}\tfrac{1}{2}r^2\mathrm{d}\theta.$$

❓ The argument given above is based on figure 2.7 in which

(i) $\delta\theta$ is positive

(ii) r increases as θ increases.

Consider how the argument must be adapted if

(a) $\delta\theta$ is negative

(b) r decreases as θ increases

(c) both (a) and (b).

Note that the final result remains the same in all cases.

EXAMPLE 2.3

Find the area of the inner loop of the limaçon $r = 1 + 2\cos\theta$ drawn in figure 2.5.

SOLUTION

The inner loop is formed as θ varies from $\dfrac{2\pi}{3}$ to $\dfrac{4\pi}{3}$, so its area is

$$\int_{2\pi/3}^{4\pi/3}\tfrac{1}{2}(1+2\cos\theta)^2\mathrm{d}\theta = \int_{2\pi/3}^{4\pi/3}\tfrac{1}{2}(1+4\cos\theta + 4\cos^2\theta)\mathrm{d}\theta$$

$$= \int_{2\pi/3}^{4\pi/3}\left(\tfrac{1}{2} + 2\cos\theta + (1+\cos 2\theta)\right)\mathrm{d}\theta \qquad \overset{\frown}{\underset{\smile}{\boxed{\text{using } \cos^2\theta = \tfrac{1}{2}(1+\cos 2\theta)}}}$$

$$= \left[\frac{3\theta}{2} + 2\sin\theta + \tfrac{1}{2}\sin 2\theta\right]_{2\pi/3}^{4\pi/3}$$

$$= \pi - \frac{3\sqrt{3}}{2}.$$

Note

Even though r is negative for $\dfrac{2\pi}{3} < \theta < \dfrac{4\pi}{3}$, the integrand $\frac{1}{2}r^2$ is always positive, so there is no problem of 'negative areas' as there is with curves below the x axis in cartesian co-ordinates.

ACTIVITY

For the limaçon $r = 1 + 2\cos\theta$ find

(i) the total area contained by the outer loop

(ii) the area between the two loops.

1 Check that $\int \frac{1}{2}r^2 d\theta$ gives the area of the circle $r = 10\cos\theta$ correctly when the integral is evaluated from $-\frac{\pi}{2}$ to $\frac{\pi}{2}$ or from 0 to π. What happens when the integration is from 0 to 2π?

2 Find the area bounded by the spiral $r = \frac{4\theta}{\pi}$ from $\theta = 0$ to $\theta = 2\pi$ and the initial line.

3 Find the areas of the two portions into which the line $\theta = \frac{\pi}{2}$ divides the upper half of the cardioid $r = 8(1 + \cos\theta)$.

4 The diagram below shows the *equiangular spiral* $r = ae^{k\theta}$, where a and k are positive constants, and the lines $\theta = 0$ and $\theta = \frac{\pi}{4}$. Prove that the areas of the regions A, B, C, ... between these lines and successive whorls form a geometric sequence, and find its common ratio.

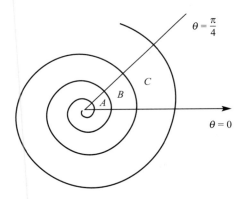

5 Sketch *Bernoulli's lemniscate* (ribbon bow) $r^2 = a^2\cos 2\theta$, and find the area of one of its loops.

6 The interior of the circle $r = 3a\cos\theta$ is divided into two parts by the cardioid $r = a(1 + \cos\theta)$. Find the area of the part whose boundary passes through the origin.

[**MEI**]

7 A curve is defined by the parametric equations $x = f(t)$, $y = g(t)$. By differentiating the relation $\tan\theta = \frac{y}{x}$ with respect to t show that

$$r^2\frac{d\theta}{dt} = x\frac{dy}{dt} - y\frac{dx}{dt}.$$

As t increases from t_1 to t_2 the point on the curve moves from P_1 to P_2, and θ increases. Prove that the area of the sector OP_1P_2 is

$$\frac{1}{2}\int_{t_1}^{t_2}\left(x\frac{dy}{dt} - y\frac{dx}{dt}\right)dt.$$

8 The arc PQ is defined by $x = t^2$, $y = t^3$, $1 \le t \le 2$. Use Question 7 to find the area of the sector bounded by this arc, OP and OQ.

9 Sketch the *astroid* $x = a\cos^3 t$, $y = a\sin^3 t$, and find the area it encloses.

10 Prove that the area enclosed by the curve

$$x = a\cos t + b\sin t, \; y = c\cos t + d\sin t$$

is $\pi\left|ad - bc\right|$.

11 (i) Sketch the curve with polar equation $r = a\sin 3\theta$ for $0 \le \theta \le \pi$, where a is a positive constant. Use a continuous line for sections where $r > 0$, and a broken line for sections where $r < 0$.

(ii) Find the area enclosed by one loop of this curve.

The point P on the curve corresponds to $\theta = \frac{1}{4}\pi$.

(iii) Mark the point P on your sketch, and give the co-ordinates of P in polar and in cartesian form.

You are given that the cartesian equation of the curve is

$$x^4 + 2x^2y^2 + y^4 = 3ax^2y - ay^3.$$

(iv) Differentiate this cartesian equation to obtain an equation involving x, y and $\dfrac{dy}{dx}$.

(v) Find the gradient of the curve at the point P.

[MEI]

12 A curve has polar equation $r = 2\sqrt{\cos 2\theta}$, for $-\frac{1}{4}\pi \le \theta \le \frac{1}{4}\pi$.

(i) Sketch the curve.

(ii) Find the area of the region enclosed by the curve.

(iii) By first writing the polar equation of the curve as $r^2 = 4(\cos^2\theta - \sin^2\theta)$, show that the cartesian equation of the curve is

$$x^4 + 2x^2y^2 + y^4 - 4x^2 + 4y^2 = 0.$$

(iv) Differentiate this cartesian equation to obtain a relationship between x, y and $\dfrac{dy}{dx}$.

(v) If P is a point on the curve where $\dfrac{dy}{dx} = 0$, show that OP $= \sqrt{2}$, where O is the origin.

(vi) Find the *polar* co-ordinates of the two points on the curve where $\dfrac{dy}{dx} = 0$.

[MEI]

LIMAÇONS

(i) Figure 2.8 shows a circle with centre A and diameter OB = 2a. A line through O meets the circle again at Q, and P, P′ are points on this line such that PQ = QP′ = k (a fixed distance). Draw this figure, taking a = 3 cm and k = 8 cm. Draw many positions of the line as Q moves around the circle, and draw a freehand curve through the marked points P and P′. This curve is called a *limaçon*. Draw another limaçon with a = k = 3 cm.

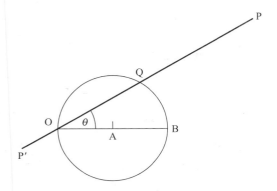

Figure 2.8

(ii) Without further detailed drawing, sketch other limaçons, noting the general shape **(a)** when k > 2a **(b)** when k < 2a. What happens when k is very large, or when k is close to zero?

(iii) Prove that the polar equation of the limaçon is $r = k + 2a\cos\theta$, and explain how this gives the point P′ as well as the point P.

(iv) Find the area enclosed by the limaçon $r = k + 2a\cos\theta$ when $k \geqslant 2a$.

(v) Prove that the special limaçon for which k = 2a is a cardioid.

(vi) The special limaçon for which k = a is called the *trisectrix*; this is the curve drawn in part **(i)** of Example 2.2. As its name indicates, the trisectrix can be used for trisecting an angle (one of the famous Greek construction problems, which cannot be solved by straight edge and compasses alone), as follows.

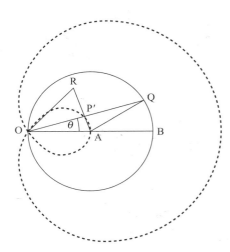

Figure 2.9

Draw angle BOR equal to the angle which is to be trisected, making OR equal to the radius *a*. Let RA meet the inner loop of the trisectrix at P'. Then angle BOP' is one third of angle BOR.

Prove this by finding angles OQA, OAQ, QAP', RAO, BOR in terms of θ.

[**Hint**: Look for three isosceles triangles.]

(vii) The limaçon is also the locus of a point fixed at a distance *a* from the centre of a circular disc of radius $\frac{1}{2}k$ which rolls without slipping around a fixed circle also of radius $\frac{1}{2}k$. To prove this, copy figure 2.8 and complete the parallelogram PQAA'. Then draw the circle *C* with centre A and radius $\frac{1}{2}k$, and the circle *C'* with centre A' and radius $\frac{1}{2}k$. Let these circles touch at T, let *C* meet AB at V, and let PA' produced meet *C'* at V'.

Prove that arc TV = arc TV', so that *C'* can be rolled around *C* until V' coincides with V. Thus V' is a point fixed on the rolling circle *C'*. But P is a fixed distance *a* from A' along V'A' since A'P = AQ, and therefore P is a fixed point of the circular disc bounded by *C'*. Note that if *k* = 2*a* then P is on the circle *C'* (giving a cardioid), and that if *k* < 2*a* then P is outside *C'*, as if on the flange of a wheel.

(viii) Yet another way of drawing a limaçon is to let O be a fixed point at a distance *a* from the centre of a base-circle of radius $\frac{1}{2}k$. Then with any point T on the base-circle as centre, draw the circle which passes through O. These circles all touch the limaçon.

Draw a limaçon by this method – it is worth doing carefully, for the result is beautiful. If you want to see why this works, look again at the diagram that you drew in (vii), and explain why TO = TP and why P moves at right angles to TP.

Historical note

These curves first appear in a book published by Albrecht Dürer in 1525, drawn by what is essentially the rolling circle method of (vii). Between 1630 and 1640 G.P. de Roberval developed pre-calculus methods for drawing tangents: he named one of his examples the 'limaçon de monsieur Pascal', referring to its inventor Étienne Pascal, the father of Blaise Pascal.

KEY POINTS

1 The principal polar co-ordinates (r, θ) are those for which $r > 0$ and $-\pi < \theta \leq \pi$.

2 $x = r\cos\theta$, $y = r\sin\theta$, $r = \sqrt{x^2 + y^2}$, $\theta = \arctan\frac{y}{x}$ ($\pm\pi$ if necessary).

3 The area of a sector is $\int_\alpha^\beta \frac{1}{2}r^2 d\theta$.

3 Complex numbers

The shortest path between two truths in the real domain passes through the complex domain.

Jacques Hadamard, 1865–1963

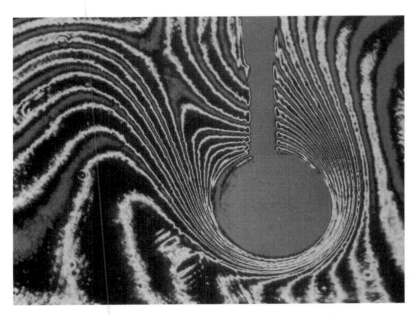

Figure 3.1 *Graphical representation of fluid-flow around a pipe*

Complex numbers may appear to be a mere mathematical curiosity but this is far from the truth. They have many applications in the real world. For example, electrical engineers use j to analyse oscillating currents. Physicists have found that imaginary numbers provide the best language for describing some real-world phenomena, such as the flow of fluid around a pipe or solutions to differential equations modelling shock absorbers.

de Moivre's theorem

First a reminder from *Pure Mathematics* 4 (page 35): to multiply two complex numbers in polar form you *multiply* their moduli and *add* their arguments:

if $z_1 = r_1(\cos\theta_1 + j\sin\theta_1)$ and $z_2 = r_2(\cos\theta_2 + j\sin\theta_2)$ then

$z_1 z_2 = r_1 r_2[\cos(\theta_1 + \theta_2) + j\sin(\theta_1 + \theta_2)]$.

Much can be achieved by using this repeatedly with just a single complex number z of modulus 1 (and so concentrating on what happens to the argument).

For if $z = \cos\theta + j\sin\theta$

then $z^2 = \cos(\theta + \theta) + j\sin(\theta + \theta) = \cos 2\theta + j\sin 2\theta,$

$z^3 = z^2 z = \cos(2\theta + \theta) + j\sin(2\theta + \theta) = \cos 3\theta + j\sin 3\theta,$

and so on. This suggests the following general result.

DE MOIVRE'S THEOREM

If n is any integer then

$$(\cos\theta + j\sin\theta)^n = \cos n\theta + j\sin n\theta.$$

PROOF

The proof is in three parts, in which n is **(i)** positive **(ii)** zero or **(iii)** negative.

(i)   When n is a positive integer the proof is by induction.

The theorem is obviously true when $n = 1$, and if

$$(\cos\theta + j\sin\theta)^k = \cos k\theta + j\sin k\theta$$

then $(\cos\theta + j\sin\theta)^{k+1} = (\cos k\theta + j\sin k\theta)(\cos\theta + j\sin\theta)$
$$= \cos(k\theta + \theta) + j\sin(k\theta + \theta)$$
$$= \cos(k+1)\theta + j\sin(k+1)\theta$$

so by induction the theorem is true for all positive integers n.

(ii)   By definition, $z^0 = 1$ for all complex numbers $z \neq 0$. Therefore

$$(\cos\theta + j\sin\theta)^0 = 1 = \cos 0 + j\sin 0.$$

(iii)   For negative n the proof starts with the case $n = -1$. Since

$$(\cos\theta + j\sin\theta)(\cos(-\theta) + j\sin(-\theta)) = \cos(\theta - \theta) + j\sin(\theta - \theta) = 1$$

it follows that $(\cos\theta + j\sin\theta)^{-1} = \cos(-\theta) + j\sin(-\theta)$.   ①

If n is a negative integer, let $n = -m$. Then

$(\cos\theta + j\sin\theta)^n = (\cos\theta + j\sin\theta)^{-m}$
$$= [(\cos\theta + j\sin\theta)^m]^{-1}$$
$$= (\cos m\theta + j\sin m\theta)^{-1} \quad \text{using (i) for } m, \text{ which is positive}$$
$$= \cos(-m\theta) + j\sin(-m\theta) \quad \text{using ① with } m\theta \text{ in place of } \theta$$
$$= \cos n\theta + j\sin n\theta.$$

de Moivre's theorem is also useful for simplifying powers of complex numbers when the modulus is not 1. For if $z = r(\cos\theta + j\sin\theta)$ then

$$z^n = [r(\cos\theta + j\sin\theta)]^n = r^n(\cos\theta + j\sin\theta)^n = r^n(\cos n\theta + j\sin n\theta).$$

EXAMPLE 3.1

Evaluate **(i)** $\left(\cos\dfrac{\pi}{8} + j\sin\dfrac{\pi}{8}\right)^{12}$ **(ii)** $\left(\sqrt{3} + j\right)^{5}$.

SOLUTION

(i) By de Moivre's theorem

$$\left(\cos\frac{\pi}{8} + j\sin\frac{\pi}{8}\right)^{12} = \cos\left(12 \times \frac{\pi}{8}\right) + j\sin\left(12 \times \frac{\pi}{8}\right)$$

$$= \left(\cos\frac{3\pi}{2}\right) + j\sin\left(\frac{3\pi}{2}\right) = -j.$$

(ii) First convert to polar form:

$$z = \sqrt{3} + j \Rightarrow |z| = \sqrt{3 + 1} = 2, \arg z = \arctan\left(\frac{1}{\sqrt{3}}\right) = \frac{\pi}{6}.$$

So $\left(\sqrt{3} + j\right)^{5} = 2^{5}\left(\cos\dfrac{\pi}{6} + j\sin\dfrac{\pi}{6}\right)^{5}$

$$= 32\left(\cos\frac{5\pi}{6} + j\sin\frac{5\pi}{6}\right)$$

$$= 32\left(-\frac{\sqrt{3}}{2} + \frac{j}{2}\right)$$

$$= -16\sqrt{3} + 16j.$$

Historical note

Abraham de Moivre (1667–1754) came to England from France as a Huguenot refugee at the age of eighteen and spent the rest of his long life in London. In papers from 1707 onwards he made use of 'his' theorem, though he never published it explicitly.

EXERCISE 3A

1 Use de Moivre's theorem to evaluate the following.

(i) $\left(\cos\dfrac{\pi}{4} + j\sin\dfrac{\pi}{4}\right)^{15}$

(ii) $\left(\cos\dfrac{\pi}{3} + j\sin\dfrac{\pi}{3}\right)^{-8}$

(iii) $\left(\cos-\dfrac{\pi}{12} + j\sin-\dfrac{\pi}{12}\right)^{10}$

(iv) $\left(\cos\dfrac{7\pi}{8} - j\sin\dfrac{7\pi}{8}\right)^{6}$

[**Hint for (iv)**: $\cos\theta - j\sin\theta = \cos(-\theta) + j\sin(-\theta)$]

2 By converting to polar form and using de Moivre's theorem, find the following in the form $x + jy$, giving x and y as exact expressions or correct to 3 decimal places.

(i) $(1 - \sqrt{3}j)^{4}$

(ii) $(-2 + 2j)^{7}$

(iii) $(0.6 + 0.8j)^{-5}$

(iv) $(\sqrt{27} + 3j)^{6}$

3 Simplify the following.

(i) $(\cos(-\alpha) + j\sin(-\alpha))^{8}$

(ii) $\dfrac{(\cos\beta + j\sin\beta)^{3}}{(\cos\beta - j\sin\beta)^{-5}}$

(iii) $(\cos^{2}\gamma + j\sin\gamma\cos\gamma)^{10}$

(iv) $(1 + \cos 2\delta + j\sin 2\delta)^{-4}$

4 Deduce from de Moivre's theorem that $(\cos\theta - j\sin\theta)^{n} = \cos n\theta - j\sin n\theta$

(i) by putting $\theta = -\phi$

(ii) by using conjugates.

Using de Moivre's theorem

One of the reasons for the general acceptance of complex numbers during the eighteenth century was their usefulness in producing results involving only *real* numbers; these results could also be obtained without using complex numbers, but often only with considerably greater trouble. de Moivre's theorem is a good source of such examples.

EXAMPLE 3.2

Express $\cos 5\theta$ in terms of $\cos\theta$.

SOLUTION

By de Moivre's theorem

$$\cos 5\theta + j\sin 5\theta = (\cos\theta + j\sin\theta)^5$$
$$= c^5 + 5jc^4s - 10c^3s^2 - 10jc^2s^3 + 5cs^4 + js^5$$

(where c and s are used as abbreviations for $\cos\theta$ and $\sin\theta$ respectively).

Equating real parts:

$$\cos 5\theta = c^5 - 10c^3s^2 + 5cs^4.$$

But $\quad s^2 = 1 - c^2$

so $\quad \cos 5\theta = c^5 - 10c^3(1 - c^2) + 5c(1 - c^2)^2$
$$= c^5 - 10c^3 + 10c^5 + 5c - 10c^3 + 5c^5.$$

Therefore $\cos 5\theta = 16\cos^5\theta - 20\cos^3\theta + 5\cos\theta$.

ACTIVITY

(i)   Check that the above expression for $\cos 5\theta$ gives the correct results when $\theta = 0$ and when $\theta = \pi$.

(ii)   By equating imaginary parts find $\sin 5\theta$ in terms of $\sin\theta$.

Notice that de Moivre not only gives a straightforward solution of the original problem, but also gives the expression for $\sin 5\theta$ with very little extra work – two for the price of one!

Example 3.2 gave a multiple-angle formula in terms of powers; it is sometimes useful (e.g. when integrating) to do the reverse. For this you need the following deduction from the main theorem:

if $\quad z = \cos\theta + j\sin\theta$

then $\quad z^n = \cos n\theta + j\sin n\theta$

and $\quad z^{-n} = \cos(-n\theta) + j\sin(-n\theta) = \cos n\theta - j\sin n\theta.$

Therefore $\quad \cos n\theta = \dfrac{z^n + z^{-n}}{2}$

and $\quad \sin n\theta = \dfrac{z^n - z^{-n}}{2j}.$

EXAMPLE 3.3

Express $\cos^5\theta$ in terms of multiple angles.

SOLUTION

Let $z = \cos\theta + j\sin\theta$.

Then $\quad 2\cos\theta = z + z^{-1}$

$\Rightarrow \quad 2^5\cos^5\theta = (z + z^{-1})^5$

$\quad\quad\quad\quad\quad = z^5 + 5z^3 + 10z + 10z^{-1} + 5z^{-3} + z^{-5}$

$\quad\quad\quad\quad\quad = (z^5 + z^{-5}) + 5(z^3 + z^{-3}) + 10(z + z^{-1})$

$\quad\quad\quad\quad\quad = 2\cos 5\theta + 10\cos 3\theta + 20\cos\theta$

$\Rightarrow \quad\quad \cos^5\theta = \dfrac{\cos 5\theta + 5\cos 3\theta + 10\cos\theta}{16}$

| ACTIVITY

Use a similar method to express $\sin^5\theta$ in terms of multiple angles.

EXERCISE 3B

1 Prove that $\cos 4\theta = c^4 - 6c^2s^2 + s^4$ and $\sin 4\theta = 4c^3s - 4cs^3$, where $c = \cos\theta$, $s = \sin\theta$.

Use these results to find $\tan 4\theta$ as a rational function of $\tan\theta$.

$\left[\textbf{Hint: } \text{Put } \tan 4\theta = \dfrac{\sin 4\theta}{\cos 4\theta} \text{ and divide throughout by } c^4.\right]$

2 Find the expressions for $\cos 3\theta$ and $\sin 3\theta$ given by de Moivre's theorem. Hence express

(i) $\cos 3\theta$ in terms of $\cos\theta$

(ii) $\sin 3\theta$ in terms of $\sin\theta$

(iii) $\tan 3\theta$ in terms of $\tan\theta$.

3 Find $\cos 6\theta$ and $\dfrac{\sin 6\theta}{\sin\theta}$ in terms of $\cos\theta$.

4 If $c = \cos\theta$, $s = \sin\theta$, $t = \tan\theta$ show that

$$\cos n\theta = c^n - {}^nC_2 c^{n-2}s^2 + {}^nC_4 c^{n-4}s^4 - \cdots$$
$$= c^n(1 - {}^nC_2 t^2 + {}^nC_4 t^4 - \cdots)$$

and $\quad \sin n\theta = {}^nC_1 c^{n-1}s - {}^nC_3 c^{n-3}s^3 + \cdots$

$$= c^n({}^nC_1 t - {}^nC_3 t^3 + \cdots).$$

Hence find $\tan n\theta$ in terms of t.

5 Express each of the following in terms of multiple angles.

(i) $\cos^4\theta$

(ii) $\sin^5\theta$

(iii) $\sin^6\theta$

(iv) $\cos^3\theta\sin^4\theta$

(v) $\cos^4\theta\sin^3\theta$

6 Prove that $\cos^m\theta \sin^n\theta$ can be expressed in terms of the cosines of multiple angles if n is even, and in terms of the sines of multiple angles if n is odd.

7 Use your previous results to find these integrals.

(i) $\displaystyle\int \sin^6\theta\,d\theta$ **(ii)** $\displaystyle\int_0^{\pi/2} \cos^3\theta \sin^4\theta\,d\theta$ **(iii)** $\displaystyle\int_0^{\pi} \cos^4\theta \sin^3\theta\,d\theta$

8 Use $\cos n\theta = \dfrac{z^n + z^{-n}}{2}$ to express

$$\cos\theta + \cos 3\theta + \cos 5\theta + \cdots + \cos(2n-1)\theta$$

as a geometric series in terms of z. Hence find this sum in terms of θ.

9 (i) Given that $z = \cos\theta + j\sin\theta$, write down z^n and $\dfrac{1}{z^n}$ in the form $a + jb$. Simplify $z^n + \dfrac{1}{z^n}$ and $z^n - \dfrac{1}{z^n}$.

(ii) By considering z^5, show that $\tan 5\theta = \dfrac{5\tan\theta - 10\tan^3\theta + \tan^5\theta}{1 - 10\tan^2\theta + 5\tan^4\theta}$.

(iii) By considering $\left(z - \dfrac{1}{z}\right)^2\left(z + \dfrac{1}{z}\right)^4$ find the constants p, q, r and s such that

$$\sin^2\theta\cos^4\theta = p + q\cos 2\theta + r\cos 4\theta + s\cos 6\theta.$$

[MEI]

10 (i) Given that $z = \cos\theta + j\sin\theta$, write down z^n and $\dfrac{1}{z^n}$ in the form $a + jb$. Simplify $z^n + \dfrac{1}{z^n}$ and $z^n - \dfrac{1}{z^n}$.

(ii) Expand $\left(z - \dfrac{1}{z}\right)^4\left(z + \dfrac{1}{z}\right)^2$, and hence find the constants p, q, r and s such that $\sin^4\theta\cos^2\theta = p + q\cos 2\theta + r\cos 4\theta + s\cos 6\theta$.

(iii) Using a suitable substitution, and your answer to part **(ii)**, show that

$$\int_1^2 x^4\sqrt{4 - x^2}\,dx = \frac{4\pi}{3} + \sqrt{3}.$$

[MEI]

11 By expressing $\cos^{2n}\theta$ in terms of cosines of multiple angles, prove that

$$\int_0^{\pi} \cos^{2n}\theta\,d\theta = \frac{(2n)!\pi}{2^{2n}(n!)^2}.$$

What is $\displaystyle\int_0^{\pi} \cos^{2n+1}\theta\,d\theta$?

Complex exponents

When multiplying complex numbers in polar form you add the arguments, and when multiplying powers of the same base you add the exponents. This suggests that there may be a link between the familiar expression $\cos\theta + j\sin\theta$ and the seemingly remote territory of the exponential function. This was first noticed in 1714 by the young Englishman Roger Cotes, two years before his death at the age of 28 (when Newton remarked 'If Cotes had lived we might have known something'), and made widely known through an influential book published by Euler in 1748.

Let $z = \cos\theta + j\sin\theta$. Since j behaves like any other constant in algebraic manipulation, to differentiate z with respect to θ you simply differentiate the real and imaginary parts separately. This gives

$$\begin{aligned}
\frac{dz}{d\theta} &= -\sin\theta + j\cos\theta \\
&= j^2\sin\theta + j\cos\theta \\
&= j(\cos\theta + j\sin\theta) \\
&= jz.
\end{aligned}$$

So $z = \cos\theta + j\sin\theta$ is a solution of the differential equation $\dfrac{dz}{d\theta} = jz$.

If j continues to behave like any other constant when it is used as an index, then the general solution of $\dfrac{dz}{d\theta} = jz$ is $z = e^{j\theta} + c$, where c is a constant (see *Pure Mathematics 2*, page 158).

Therefore $\cos\theta + j\sin\theta = e^{j\theta} + c$.

Moreover, since $\theta = 0 \Rightarrow \cos\theta + j\sin\theta = \cos 0 + j\sin 0 = 1$ and $e^{j\theta} + c = e^0 + c = 1 + c$, it follows that $c = 0$ and $\cos\theta + j\sin\theta = e^{j\theta}$.

The problem with this argument is that you have no way of knowing how j behaves as an index. But this does not matter. Since no meaning has yet been given to e^z when z is complex, the following *definition* can be made, suggested by this work with differential equations but not dependent on it:

$$e^{j\theta} = \cos\theta + j\sin\theta.$$

Note

The particular case when $\theta = \pi$ gives $e^{j\pi} = \cos\pi + j\sin\pi = -1$, so that

$$e^{j\pi} + 1 = 0.$$

This remarkable statement, linking the five fundamental numbers 0, 1, j, e, π, the three fundamental operations of addition, multiplication and exponentiation, and the fundamental relation of equality, has been described as a 'mathematical poem'.

The first use of $e^{j\theta}$ is simply as a more compact way of writing familiar expressions. For example, the polar form $r(\cos\theta + j\sin\theta)$ can now be abbreviated to $re^{j\theta}$, and de Moivre's theorem becomes the seemingly obvious statement

$$(e^{j\theta})^n = e^{jn\theta} \text{ for all rational } n.$$

The definition of e^z for any complex number z is now fairly obvious. Since you naturally want to preserve the basic property $e^{a+b} = e^a \times e^b$, it follows that if $z = x + jy$ then $e^z = e^x \times e^{jy}$.

This suggests the *definition*

$$e^z = e^x(\cos y + j\sin y).$$

Notice that, when $y = 0$, $e^z = e^x$, so that when z is real this definition of e^z gives the exponential function you have used until now. Also, taking $x = 0$, $e^{jy} = \cos y + j \sin y$, agreeing with the definition suggested by the differential equation.

ACTIVITY

Prove that $e^{z + 2\pi nj} = e^z$. This means that the exponential function is periodic, with the imaginary period $2\pi j$.

EXAMPLE 3.4

Given two complex numbers, z and w, prove from the definition that

$$e^{z+w} = e^z \times e^w.$$

SOLUTION

Let $z = x + jy$ and $w = u + jv$. Then

$$\begin{aligned}
e^z \times e^w &= e^x(\cos y + j \sin y) \times e^u(\cos v + j \sin v) \\
&= e^x e^u(\cos y + j \sin y)(\cos v + j \sin v) \\
&= e^{x+u}(\cos(y + v) + j \sin(y + v)) \\
&= e^{x+u+j(y+v)} \\
&= e^{z+w}.
\end{aligned}$$

Since $e^{j\theta} = \cos \theta + j \sin \theta$ and $e^{-j\theta} = \cos(-\theta) + j \sin(-\theta) = \cos \theta - j \sin \theta$, it follows that

$$\cos \theta = \frac{e^{j\theta} + e^{-j\theta}}{2} \quad \text{and} \quad \sin \theta = \frac{e^{j\theta} - e^{-j\theta}}{2j}.$$

These are essentially the same as the results which were used in Example 3.3.

EXAMPLE 3.5

Prove that $1 + e^{j\theta} = 2 \cos \frac{\theta}{2} e^{j\theta/2}$.

SOLUTION

The factor $e^{j\theta/2}$ on the right-hand side suggests writing each term on the left-hand side as a multiple of $e^{j\theta/2}$.

$$1 = e^{j\theta/2} \times e^{-j\theta/2} \quad \text{and} \quad e^{j\theta} = e^{j\theta/2} \times e^{j\theta/2}.$$

Therefore $\quad 1 + e^{j\theta} = e^{j\theta/2}(e^{-j\theta/2} + e^{j\theta/2})$

$$= e^{j\theta/2} \times 2 \cos \frac{\theta}{2}, \text{ as required.}$$

Note

You should remember the result of Example 3.5 as it will be useful in the work of the next section. See Question 6 of Exercise 3C for an alternative method.

1 Express e^z in the form $x + jy$, where z is the given complex number.

(i) $-j\pi$ **(ii)** $\dfrac{j\pi}{4}$ **(iii)** $\dfrac{2 + 5j\pi}{6}$ **(iv)** $3 - 4j$

2 Find all the solutions of $e^z = e^3$, and plot some of them on an Argand diagram.

3 Find all the solutions of $e^z = \dfrac{1 - \sqrt{3}j}{2e^4}$, and plot some of them on an Argand diagram.

4 Find all the values of z for which $e^{z^*} = (e^z)^*$.

5 Prove that $1 - e^{j\theta} = -2j \sin \dfrac{\theta}{2} e^{j\theta/2}$.

6 Plot the points 0, 1, $e^{j\theta}$, $1 + e^{j\theta}$ on an Argand diagram.

What sort of quadrilateral do these points form?

Use the geometry of this quadrilateral to prove again the results of Example 3.5 and Question 5.

7 Prove that $(1 + e^{2j\theta})^n = 2^n \cos^n\theta\, e^{jn\theta}$.

8 If $z = f(p) + jg(p)$, where p is a real parameter then the derivative and integral of z with respect to p are defined by $\dfrac{dz}{dp} = f'(p) + jg'(p)$ and

$$\int z\, dp = \int f(p)\, dp + j\int g(p)\, dp.$$

Prove that if $z = e^{\alpha p}$ where α is a fixed complex number, then $\dfrac{dz}{dp} = \alpha e^{\alpha p}$ and

$$\int z\, dp = \dfrac{e^{\alpha p}}{\alpha} + c.$$

9 The position at time t of a point Z moving in an Argand diagram is given by $z = re^{j\theta}$, where r and θ depend on t.

Find $\dfrac{dz}{dt}$ and $\dfrac{d^2z}{dt^2}$, and deduce the radial and transverse components of the velocity and acceleration of Z. (The *radial* and *transverse* directions are respectively parallel and perpendicular to $\overrightarrow{OZ}$.)

10 Let $C = \int e^{3x}\cos 2x\, dx$ and $S = \int e^{3x}\sin 2x\, dx$.

Show that $C + jS = \dfrac{e^{(3+2j)x}}{3 + 2j} + A$, where A is a constant. Hence find C and S.

11 Find $\int e^{ax}\cos bx\, dx$ and $\int e^{ax}\sin bx\, dx$

(i) by using integration by parts twice

(ii) by using the method of Question 10.

Which method do you prefer?

Summations using complex numbers

This section shows how complex numbers can be used to evaluate certain real sums. It may be possible to do these summations without using complex numbers (e.g. by induction, once you know the answer), but this is considerably more awkward. Sometimes it is worth setting out to do *more* than is required, as in the next example.

EXAMPLE 3.6

Find a simplified expression for the sum of the series

$$1 + {}^nC_1 \cos\theta + {}^nC_2 \cos 2\theta + {}^nC_3 \cos 3\theta + \cdots + \cos n\theta.$$

SOLUTION

At first sight this series suggests the binomial expansion $(1 + \cos\theta)^n$: the coefficients $1\ (= {}^nC_0)$, ${}^nC_1$, ${}^nC_2$, ..., $1\ (= {}^nC_n)$ are right, but there are multiple angles, $\cos r\theta$, instead of powers of cosines, $\cos^r\theta$. This indicates that de Moivre's theorem can be used. The trick is to introduce the corresponding sine series too.

Let $C = 1 + {}^nC_1 \cos\theta + {}^nC_2 \cos 2\theta + {}^nC_3 \cos 3\theta + \cdots + \cos n\theta$

and $S = {}^nC_1 \sin\theta + {}^nC_2 \sin 2\theta + {}^nC_3 \sin 3\theta + \cdots + \sin n\theta.$

Then $C + jS = 1 + {}^nC_1(\cos\theta + j\sin\theta) + {}^nC_2(\cos 2\theta + j\sin 2\theta) + \cdots + (\cos n\theta + j\sin n\theta)$

$$= 1 + {}^nC_1 e^{j\theta} + {}^nC_2 e^{j2\theta} + \cdots + e^{jn\theta}$$

$$= 1 + {}^nC_1 e^{j\theta} + {}^nC_2 (e^{j\theta})^2 + \cdots + (e^{j\theta})^n.$$

> Using de Moivre's theorem: $e^{jr\theta} = (e^{j\theta})^r$.

This is now recognisable as a binomial expansion, so that

$$C + jS = (1 + e^{j\theta})^n.$$

To find C you need to find the real part of $(1 + e^{j\theta})^n$, and here Example 3.5 is useful:

$$(1 + e^{j\theta})^n = \left(2\cos\frac{\theta}{2} e^{j\theta/2}\right)^n$$

$$= 2^n \cos^n\frac{\theta}{2} e^{jn\theta/2}$$

$$= 2^n \cos^n\frac{\theta}{2}\left(\cos\frac{n\theta}{2} + j\sin\frac{n\theta}{2}\right).$$

Taking the real part, $C = 2^n \cos^n\frac{\theta}{2} \cos\frac{n\theta}{2}.$

I ACTIVITY

State the result obtained by equating imaginary parts.

1 Let $C = 1 + \cos\theta + \cos 2\theta + \cdots + \cos(n-1)\theta$

and $S = \sin\theta + \sin 2\theta + \cdots + \sin(n-1)\theta$.

Show that $C + jS$ is a geometric progression with common ratio $e^{j\theta}$

and sum $\dfrac{1 - e^{jn\theta}}{1 - e^{j\theta}}$.

By multiplying the numerator and denominator of this sum by $1 - e^{-j\theta}$, show

that $C = \dfrac{1 - \cos\theta + \cos(n-1)\theta - \cos n\theta}{2 - 2\cos\theta}$ and find S.

2 (i) Show the points 2 and $2 + \cos\dfrac{2\pi}{3} + j\sin\dfrac{2\pi}{3}$ on an Argand diagram, and

hence show that $2 + \cos\dfrac{2\pi}{3} + j\sin\dfrac{2\pi}{3} = \sqrt{3}e^{j\pi/6}$.

(ii) Deduce that

$$\sum_{r=0}^{n} {}^{n}C_{r}2^{n-r}\cos\dfrac{2r\pi}{3} = 3^{n/2}\cos\dfrac{n\pi}{6}.$$

(iii) State the corresponding result for sines.

3 You are given that $w = 1 - e^{j\theta}\cos\theta$, where $0 < \theta < \frac{1}{2}\pi$.

(i) Express $e^{jk\theta}$ and $e^{-jk\theta}$ in the form $a + jb$, and show that $w = -je^{j\theta}\sin\theta$.

(ii) Find $|w|$ and $\arg w$.

Hence write down the modulus and argument of each of the two square roots of w.

Series C and S are defined by

$$C = \cos\theta\cos\theta + \cos 2\theta\cos^2\theta + \cos 3\theta\cos^3\theta + \cdots + \cos n\theta\cos^n\theta$$
$$S = \sin\theta\cos\theta + \sin 2\theta\cos^2\theta + \sin 3\theta\cos^3\theta + \cdots + \sin n\theta\cos^n\theta.$$

(iii) Show that $C + jS$ is a geometric series, and write down the sum of this series.

(iv) Using the results in part **(i)**, or otherwise, show that $C = \dfrac{\sin n\theta\cos^{n+1}\theta}{\sin\theta}$,

and find a similar expression for S.

[MEI]

4 (i) Given that $z = \cos\theta + j\sin\theta$, express z^2, z^3, and z^n in the form $a + jb$.

The infinite series C and S are defined as follows:

$$C = 1 + \frac{1}{3}\cos\theta + \frac{1}{9}\cos 2\theta + \frac{1}{27}\cos 3\theta + \cdots + \frac{1}{3^n}\cos n\theta + \cdots$$
$$S = \frac{1}{3}\sin\theta + \frac{1}{9}\sin 2\theta + \frac{1}{27}\sin 3\theta + \cdots + \frac{1}{3^n}\sin n\theta + \cdots.$$

(ii) Express $C + jS$ in terms of z, and show that it is a geometric series.

(iii) Write down, in terms of z, the sum to infinity of this geometric series.

(iv) Express, in terms of θ, the sum to infinity of **(a)** C **(b)** S.

(v) Show that $|C + jS| = \dfrac{3}{\sqrt{10 - 6\cos\theta}}$.

[MEI]

5 (i) Write down, in the form $a + jb$, the following complex numbers: $e^{j\theta}$, $e^{jn\theta}$ and $e^{-jn\theta}$.

(ii) Show that $(1 - \frac{1}{2}e^{2j\theta})(1 - \frac{1}{2}e^{-2j\theta}) = \frac{5}{4} - \cos 2\theta$.

The infinite series C and S are defined as follows:

$$C = \cos\theta + \frac{1}{2}\cos 3\theta + \frac{1}{4}\cos 5\theta + \frac{1}{8}\cos 7\theta + \cdots + \frac{1}{2^{r-1}}\cos(2r-1)\theta + \cdots$$

$$S = \sin\theta + \frac{1}{2}\sin 3\theta + \frac{1}{4}\sin 5\theta + \frac{1}{8}\sin 7\theta + \cdots + \frac{1}{2^{r-1}}\sin(2r-1)\theta + \cdots.$$

(iii) Show that $C + jS = \dfrac{4e^{j\theta} - 2e^{-j\theta}}{5 - 4\cos 2\theta}$.

(iv) Hence find expressions for C and S in terms of $\cos\theta$, $\sin\theta$ and $\cos 2\theta$ only.

[MEI]

6 (i) Express the complex number $e^{jn\theta}$ in the form $a + bj$.

(ii) Simplify $\frac{1}{2}(e^{j\theta} + e^{-j\theta})$ and $(1 + \frac{1}{2}e^{j\theta})(1 + \frac{1}{2}e^{-j\theta})$.

Infinite series C and S are defined as follows:

$$C = \frac{\cos\theta}{2} - \frac{\cos 2\theta}{4} + \frac{\cos 3\theta}{8} - \frac{\cos 4\theta}{16} + \cdots$$

$$S = \frac{\sin\theta}{2} - \frac{\sin 2\theta}{4} + \frac{\sin 3\theta}{8} - \frac{\sin 4\theta}{16} + \cdots.$$

(iii) Show that $C + jS = \dfrac{2e^{j\theta} + 1}{5 + 4\cos\theta}$.

(iv) Hence find expressions for C and S in terms of $\cos\theta$ and $\sin\theta$.

[MEI]

7 Sum the series $\displaystyle\sum_{r=0}^{n} {}^{n}C_r \sin(\alpha + r\beta)$.

Complex roots: the roots of unity

As early as 1629 Albert Girard stated that every polynomial equation of degree n has exactly n roots (including repetitions); this was first proved by the 18-year-old Carl Friedrich Gauss 170 years later.

Therefore even the simple equation $z^n = 1$ has n roots. Of course one of these is $z = 1$, and if n is even then $z = -1$ is another. But where are the rest?

ACTIVITY

(i) Write down the two roots of $z^2 = 1$, and show them in an Argand diagram.

(ii) Use $z^3 - 1 = (z - 1)(z^2 + z + 1)$ to find the three roots of $z^3 = 1$. Show them in an Argand diagram.

(iii) Find the four roots of $z^4 = 1$, and show them in an Argand diagram.

Every root of the equation $z^n = 1$ must have unit modulus, since otherwise the modulus of z^n would not be 1. So every root is of the form $z = \cos\theta + j\sin\theta$,

and $\quad z^n = 1 \quad \Leftrightarrow \quad (\cos\theta + j\sin\theta)^n = 1$
$$\Leftrightarrow \quad \cos n\theta + j\sin n\theta = 1 \text{ (by de Moivre)}$$
$$\Leftrightarrow \quad n\theta = 2k\pi, \text{ where } k \text{ is any integer,}$$

since 1 is $(1, 0)$ or $(1, 2\pi)$ or $(1, 4\pi)$ or ... in polar form.

As k takes the values $0, 1, 2, ..., n - 1$ the corresponding values of θ are

$$0, \frac{2\pi}{n}, \frac{4\pi}{n}, ..., \frac{2(n-1)\pi}{n},$$

giving n distinct values of z. But when $k = n$ then $\theta = 2\pi$, which gives the same z as $\theta = 0$. Similarly any integer value of k larger than n differs from one of $0, 1, 2, ..., n - 1$ by a multiple of n, and so gives a value of θ differing by a multiple of 2π from one already listed; the same applies when k is any negative integer.

Therefore the equation $z^n = 1$ has precisely n roots. These are

$$z = \cos\frac{2k\pi}{n} + j\sin\frac{2k\pi}{n}, \quad k = 0, 1, 2, ..., n - 1.$$

These n complex numbers are called the nth *roots of unity*. They include $z = 1$ when $k = 0$ and, if n is even, $z = -1$ when $k = \frac{n}{2}$. It is customary to use ω (the Greek letter omega) for the root with the smallest positive argument:

$$\omega = \cos\frac{2\pi}{n} + j\sin\frac{2\pi}{n}.$$

Then, by de Moivre's theorem,

$$\omega^k = \cos\frac{2k\pi}{n} + j\sin\frac{2k\pi}{n},$$

so that the nth roots of unity may be written as

$$1, \omega, \omega^2, ..., \omega^{n-1}.$$

The complex numbers $1, \omega, \omega^2, ..., \omega^{n-1}$ are represented on an Argand diagram by the vertices of a regular n-sided polygon inscribed in the unit circle with one vertex at the point 1.

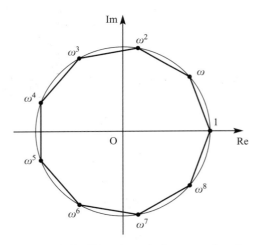

Figure 3.2 *The nine ninth roots of unity*

I ACTIVITY

Prove that $(\omega^r)^* = \omega^{n-r}$.

The sum of all the nth roots of unity is a geometric series with common ratio ω:

$$1 + \omega + \omega^2 + \cdots + \omega^{n-1} = \frac{1 - \omega^n}{1 - \omega} = 0.$$

since $\omega^n = 1$

Therefore the sum of all n of the nth roots of unity is zero.

EXAMPLE 3.7

Solve the equation $(1 + jz)^n = (1 - jz)^n$, where n is odd.

SOLUTION

The equation can be rearranged as $\left(\dfrac{1 + jz}{1 - jz}\right)^n = 1$.

By taking the nth root of both sides you have, $\dfrac{1 + jz}{1 - jz} = \alpha$, where $\alpha = e^{j\theta}$ is an nth root of unity.

Solving this for z gives $z = \dfrac{\alpha - 1}{j(\alpha + 1)}$, where since n is odd $\alpha + 1 \neq 0$.

But

$$\alpha - 1 = 2j \sin \frac{\theta}{2} e^{j\theta/2}$$

and

As in Example 3.5 and Exercise 3C Questions 5, 6.

$$\alpha + 1 = 2 \cos \frac{\theta}{2} e^{j\theta/2}.$$

Substituting these in the expression for z and simplifying gives

$$z = \frac{\sin \dfrac{\theta}{2}}{\cos \dfrac{\theta}{2}} = \tan \frac{\theta}{2}.$$

Since α is a nth root of unity, $\theta = \dfrac{2k\pi}{n}$, and so the roots are $z = \tan \dfrac{k\pi}{n}$, $k = 0, 1, 2, \ldots, n - 1$.

ACTIVITY

Work through Example 3.7 in the case when n is even. (Be careful: what is the degree of the equation now?)

EXERCISE 3E

1 Explain geometrically why the set of tenth roots of unity is the same as the set of fifth roots of unity together with their negatives.

2 If ω is a complex cube root of unity, $\omega \neq 1$, prove that

(i) $(1 + \omega)(1 + \omega^2) = 1$

(ii) $1 + \omega$ and $1 + \omega^2$ are complex cube roots of -1

(iii) $(a + b)(a + \omega b)(a + \omega^2 b) = a^3 + b^3$

(iv) $(a + b + c)(a + \omega b + \omega^2 c)(a + \omega^2 b + \omega c) = a^3 + b^3 + c^3 - 3abc.$

3 A regular hexagon is inscribed in the unit circle. One vertex is α. Give the other vertices in terms of α and ω, where ω is a complex cube root of unity.

4 The complex numbers $1, \omega, \omega^2, ..., \omega^{n-1}$ are represented as *vectors* in an Argand diagram, following 'nose to tail' in order. Explain geometrically why these form a regular polygon. Hence prove again that the sum of all the nth roots of unity is zero.

5 (i) **(a)** Draw an Argand diagram showing the points $1, \omega, \omega^2, \omega^3, \omega^4$, where $\omega = \cos\dfrac{2\pi}{5} + \mathrm{j}\sin\dfrac{2\pi}{5}$.

         (b) If $\alpha = \omega^2$ show that the points $1, \alpha, \alpha^2, \alpha^3, \alpha^4$ are the same as the points in **(a)**, but in a different order. Indicate this order by joining successive points on your diagram.

         (c) Repeat **(b)** with α replaced by β, where $\beta = \omega^3$.

     (ii) Repeat the whole of **(i)** taking $\omega = \cos\dfrac{2\pi}{6} + \mathrm{j}\sin\dfrac{2\pi}{6}$ and considering the points $1, \omega, ..., \omega^5; 1, \alpha, ..., \alpha^5; 1, \beta, ..., \beta^5$.

     (iii) Do likewise for the seventh and eighth roots of unity.

     (iv) If $\omega = \cos\dfrac{2\pi}{n} + \mathrm{j}\sin\dfrac{2\pi}{n}$ and $\alpha = \omega^m$, form a conjecture about when $\{1, \omega, \omega^2, ..., \omega^{n-1}\} = \{1, \alpha, \alpha^2, ..., \alpha^{n-1}\}$.

6 Solve the equation $z^3 = (\mathrm{j} - z)^3$.

7 Solve the equation $z^5 + z^4 + z^3 + z^2 + z + 1 = 0$.

8 Prove that all the roots of $(z - 1)^n = z^n$ have real part $\dfrac{1}{2}$.

9 Solve the equation $(\mathrm{j} - z)^n = (\mathrm{j}z - 1)^n$.

10 Solve the equation $(z + \mathrm{j})^n + (z - \mathrm{j})^n = 0$.

Complex roots: the general case

To find the nth roots of any given non-zero complex number w you have to find z such that $z^n = w$. The pattern of argument is the same as in the previous section on nth roots of unity, but adjusted to take account of the modulus s and argument ϕ of w. So let

$$z = r(\cos\theta + \mathrm{j}\sin\theta) \text{ and } w = s(\cos\phi + \mathrm{j}\sin\phi).$$

Then

$$z^n = w \iff r^n(\cos\theta + \mathrm{j}\sin\theta)^n = s(\cos\phi + \mathrm{j}\sin\phi)$$
$$\iff r^n(\cos n\theta + \mathrm{j}\sin n\theta) = s(\cos\phi + \mathrm{j}\sin\phi).$$

Two complex numbers in polar form are equal only if they have the same moduli and their arguments are equal or differ by a multiple of 2π. Therefore

$$r^n = s \text{ and } n\theta = \phi + 2k\pi, \quad \text{where } k \text{ is an integer.}$$

Since r and s are positive real numbers the equation $r^n = s$ gives the *unique* value $r = s^{1/n}$, so all the roots lie on the circle $|z| = s^{1/n}$.

The argument of z is $\theta = \dfrac{\phi + 2k\pi}{n}$. As k can take the values 0, 1, 2, ..., $n-1$, this gives n distinct complex numbers z, and (by the same argument as for the roots of unity) there are no others.

Therefore the non-zero complex number $s(\cos\phi + j\sin\phi)$ has precisely n different nth roots. These are

$$s^{1/n}\left(\cos\left(\dfrac{\phi + 2k\pi}{n}\right) + j\sin\left(\dfrac{\phi + 2k\pi}{n}\right)\right) \text{ where } k = 0, 1, 2, ..., n-1.$$

EXAMPLE 3.8

Represent $2 - 2j$ and its five fifth roots on an Argand diagram.

SOLUTION

Since $2 - 2j = 8^{1/2}\left(\cos\left(-\dfrac{\pi}{4}\right) + j\sin\left(-\dfrac{\pi}{4}\right)\right)$, the fifth roots all have modulus $8^{1/10} \approx 1.23$.

Their arguments are

$$-\dfrac{\pi}{20}, \qquad -\dfrac{\pi}{20} + \dfrac{2\pi}{5}, \qquad -\dfrac{\pi}{20} + \dfrac{4\pi}{5}, \qquad -\dfrac{\pi}{20} + \dfrac{6\pi}{5}, \qquad -\dfrac{\pi}{20} + \dfrac{8\pi}{5}$$

or (taking principal arguments in degrees) $-9°$, $63°$, $135°$, $-153°$, $-81°$.

The fifth roots are the vertices of a regular pentagon inscribed in the circle $|z| = 8^{1/10}$, as in figure 3.3.

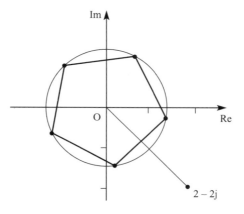

Figure 3.3

ACTIVITY

Express $8^{1/10}\left(\cos\left(-\dfrac{\pi}{20}\right) + j\sin\left(-\dfrac{\pi}{20}\right)\right)$ in the form $x + yj$, giving x and y correct to 2 decimal places.

Figure 3.3 is typical of the general case: the n nth roots of z are represented by the vertices of a regular n-gon inscribed in the circle with centre O and radius $|z|^{1/n}$. This can be useful when dealing with the geometry of regular polygons.

EXAMPLE 3.9

The vertices A_0, A_1, ..., A_{n-1} of a regular n-gon lie on a circle of unit radius with centre O. The point P is such that $\overrightarrow{OP} = 3\overrightarrow{OA_0}$.

Prove that $(PA_0)^2 + (PA_1)^2 + ... + (PA_{n-1})^2 = 10n$.

SOLUTION

Let $\omega = \cos\dfrac{2\pi}{n} + j\sin\dfrac{2\pi}{n}$, an nth root of unity. Then the vertices A_r represent the complex numbers ω^r for $r = 0, 1, ..., n-1$, and P represents 3. Therefore

$$(PA_r)^2 = \left|\omega^r - 3\right|^2 = (\omega^r - 3)(\omega^r - 3)^* = (\omega^r - 3)(\omega^{n-r} - 3)$$
$$= \omega^n - 3\omega^r - 3\omega^{n-r} + 9$$
$$= 10 - 3\omega^r - 3\omega^{n-r}, \text{ since } \omega^n = 1.$$

When this expression is summed from $r = 0$ to $r = n - 1$ the first term gives $10n$ and each of the two sums involving ω is zero, since $1 + \omega + \omega^2 + ... + \omega^{n-1} = 0$. This proves the required result.

If $w = s(\cos\phi + j\sin\phi)$ then $w^m = s^m(\cos m\phi + j\sin m\phi)$ for all integers m by de Moivre's theorem.

The complex number w^m has the n nth roots

$$s^{m/n}\left(\cos\left(\frac{m\phi + 2k\pi}{n}\right) + j\sin\left(\frac{m\phi + 2k\pi}{n}\right)\right).$$

One of these is $s^{m/n}\left(\cos\dfrac{m\phi}{n} + j\sin\dfrac{m\phi}{n}\right)$, and the notation $w^{m/n}$ is used to mean *this nth root of w^m*. This definition ensures that de Moivre's theorem is also true for rational powers, since

$$(\cos\theta + j\sin\theta)^{m/n} = \left(\cos\frac{m\theta}{n} + j\sin\frac{m\theta}{n}\right).$$

? Explain the fallacy in the following argument:

$$j = \sqrt{(-1)} = \sqrt{\frac{1}{-1}} = \frac{\sqrt{1}}{\sqrt{(-1)}} = \frac{1}{j}, \text{ so } j^2 = 1.$$

But $j^2 = -1$. Therefore $1 = -1$.

EXERCISE 3F

1 Find both square roots of $-7 + 5j$, giving your answers in the form $x + yj$ with x and y correct to 2 decimal places.

2 Find the four fourth roots of -4, giving your answers in the form $x + yj$, and show them on an Argand diagram.

3 One fourth root of w is $2 + 3j$. Find w and its other fourth roots, and represent all five points on an Argand diagram.

4 Represent the five solutions of the equation $(z - 3j)^5 = 32$ on an Argand diagram.

5 A regular heptagon (seven sides) on an Argand diagram has centre $-1 + 3j$ and one vertex at $2 + 3j$. Write down the equation whose solutions are represented by the vertices of this heptagon.

6 One of the nth roots of w is α. Prove that the other roots are $\alpha\omega$, $\alpha\omega^2$, ..., $\alpha\omega^{n-1}$ where $\omega = \cos\dfrac{2\pi}{n} + j\sin\dfrac{2\pi}{n}$. Deduce that the sum of all the nth roots of w is zero.

7 The nth roots of w are represented by vectors on an Argand diagram, with $w^{1/n}$ as a position vector and with each subsequent vector added to its predecessor. Describe the figure which is formed, and deduce again that the sum of all the nth roots is zero.

8 The vertices A_1, A_2, A_3, A_4, A_5 of a regular pentagon lie on a circle of unit radius with centre at the point O. A_1 is the mid-point of OP. Prove that

    (i) $PA_1 \times PA_2 \times PA_3 \times PA_4 \times PA_5 = 31$

    (ii) $\displaystyle\sum_{n=1}^{5} (PA_n)^2 = 25$

    (iii) $A_1A_2 \times A_1A_3 \times A_1A_4 \times A_1A_5 = 5$.

9 The fourth roots of -64 are α_1, α_2, α_3, α_4, and these complex numbers are represented by points A_1, A_2, A_3, A_4 on an Argand diagram.

    (i)   Express α_1, α_2, α_3, α_4, in the form $a + bj$.
    (ii) Draw $A_1A_2A_3A_4$ on an Argand diagram.

    With $\beta = \sqrt{3} + j$, the complex numbers $\alpha_1\beta$, $\alpha_2\beta$, $\alpha_3\beta$, $\alpha_4\beta$ are represented by points B_1, B_2, B_3, B_4 on the Argand diagram.

    (iii) Describe in detail how $A_1A_2A_3A_4$ may be transformed geometrically into $B_1B_2B_3B_4$. Hence show that $B_1B_2B_3B_4$ is a square, and state the length of a side of this square. Draw the square $B_1B_2B_3B_4$ on your diagram.
    (iv) The complex numbers $\alpha_1\beta$, $\alpha_2\beta$, $\alpha_3\beta$, $\alpha_4\beta$ are the fourth roots of a complex number w. Find w in the form $a + bj$.

                                                                                     [MEI, part]

10 (i) Express $e^{j\theta}$ and $e^{-j\theta}$ in the form $a + jb$, and show that $\dfrac{1}{1 + e^{2j\theta}} = \frac{1}{2}(1 - j\tan\theta)$.

    (ii) Solve the equation $z^5 + 32 = 0$, giving the roots in the form $re^{j\alpha}$ (where $r > 0$ and $-\pi < \alpha \leqslant \pi$). Illustrate the roots on an Argand diagram.

    (iii) If $\left(\dfrac{1 - 2w}{w}\right)^5 + 32 = 0$, show that w has the form $\frac{1}{4}(1 - j\tan\beta)$, and state the four possible values of β in the interval $-\frac{1}{2}\pi < \beta < \frac{1}{2}\pi$.

       On a separate Argand diagram, illustrate the four possible values of w.

                                                                                            [MEI]

11 (i) Express $e^{jk\theta}$ and $e^{-jk\theta}$ in the form $a + jb$, and show that

       $\dfrac{1}{1 - e^{j\theta}} = \frac{1}{2}(1 + j\cot\frac{1}{2}\theta)$.

(ii) Find the sixth roots of 8j in the form $re^{j\theta}$, where $r > 0$ and $-\pi < \theta \leqslant \pi$. Illustrate these roots on an Argand diagram.

(iii) Show that two of these sixth roots have the form $m + jn$, where m and n are integers.

(iv) Given that $\left(\sqrt{2} - \dfrac{1}{w}\right)^6 = 8j$, show that $w = p(1 + j\cot\alpha)$, stating the value of the real number p and the six possible values of α satisfying $-\frac{1}{2}\pi < \alpha < \frac{1}{2}\pi$.

[MEI]

12 (i) By considering the solutions of the equation $z^n - 1 = 0$ prove that

$$(z - \omega)(z - \omega^2)(z - \omega^3)\ldots(z - \omega^{n-1}) = z^{n-1} + z^{n-2} + \ldots + z + 1,$$

where $\omega = \cos\dfrac{2\pi}{n} + j\sin\dfrac{2\pi}{n}$.

(ii) There are n points equally spaced around the circumference of a unit circle. Prove that the product of the distances from one of these points to each of the others is n. (Question 8 part **(iii)** is the case $n = 5$.)

(iii) By finding expressions for the distances in **(ii)**, deduce that

$$\sin\frac{\pi}{n}\ \sin\frac{2\pi}{n}\ \sin\frac{3\pi}{n}\ldots\ \sin\frac{(n-1)\pi}{n} = \frac{n}{2^{n-1}}.$$

13 Find the following in polar form.

(i) $\left[32\left(\cos\dfrac{\pi}{6} + j\sin\dfrac{\pi}{6}\right)\right]^{3/5}$

(ii) $\left[343\left(\cos\dfrac{3\pi}{8} + j\sin\dfrac{3\pi}{8}\right)\right]^{-2/3}$

(iii) $\left[81\left(\cos\left(-\dfrac{\pi}{3}\right) + j\sin\left(-\dfrac{\pi}{3}\right)\right)\right]^{-1.75}$

14 (i) Find $(j^{1/2})^3$ and $(j^3)^{1/2}$. Which of these is $j^{3/2}$?

(ii) Find $(j^{1/3})^2$ and $(j^2)^{1/3}$.

(iii) Find a condition involving m and $\arg w$ which ensures that $(w^{1/n})^m = (w^m)^{1/n}$.

15 (i) Express $e^{jk\theta}$ and $e^{-jk\theta}$ in the form $a + jb$, and show that

$$e^{2j\theta} - 1 = 2je^{j\theta}\sin\theta.$$

Series C and S are defined by

$$C = \cos\theta + \cos 3\theta + \cos 5\theta + \cdots + \cos(2n-1)\theta$$
$$S = \sin\theta + \sin 3\theta + \sin 5\theta + \cdots + \sin(2n-1)\theta$$

where n is a positive integer and $0 < \theta < \dfrac{\pi}{n}$.

(ii) Show that $C + jS$ is a geometric series, and write down the sum of this series.

(iii) Show that $|C + jS| = \dfrac{\sin n\theta}{\sin\theta}$, and find $\arg(C + jS)$.

(iv) Find C and S.

The points A_0, A_1, A_2, A_3, A_4, A_5, A_6 in the Argand diagram correspond to complex numbers z_0, z_1, z_2, z_3, z_4, z_5, z_6 where $z_0 = 0$ and $z_1 = \cos\frac{1}{7}\pi + j\sin\frac{1}{7}\pi$. The points are the vertices of a regular heptagon with sides of length 1, as shown in the diagram below.

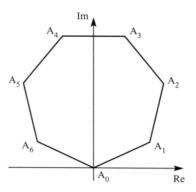

(v)   Explain why $z_n = e^{\frac{1}{7}j\pi} + e^{\frac{3}{7}j\pi} + \cdots + e^{\frac{1}{7}(2n-1)j\pi}$ for $n = 1, 2, 3, 4, 5, 6$.

Hence, or otherwise, show that $\arg(z_n) = \frac{1}{7}n\pi$ for $n = 1, 2, 3, 4, 5, 6$.

[MEI]

16   The Polish mathematician Hoëné Wronski (1778–1853) once wrote that

$$\pi = \frac{2\infty}{\sqrt{-1}}\left\{\left(1 + \sqrt{-1}\right)^{1/\infty} - \left(1 - \sqrt{-1}\right)^{1/\infty}\right\}.$$

Was Wronski wrong?

Geometrical uses of complex numbers

Your study of complex numbers started in *Pure Mathematics 4* with their origin in algebra, in connection with the solution of polynomial equations. Then the simple idea of representing a complex number as a point or a vector in the Argand diagram soon made it possible for you to use complex numbers in geometry too. Some of these geometrical applications, such as the use of mid-points, other points of subdivision, centroids, and enlargements, can be handled equally well by two-dimensional vector methods. But with other problems, especially those involving rotations or similarity, complex number methods are especially effective. For example, you have seen in the previous section some fruitful links between regular polygons and the complex roots of unity.

Much of the geometrical power of complex numbers comes from the crucial result about the multiplication of complex numbers in polar form: 'multiply the moduli, add the arguments'. This means that the effect of multiplying a complex number z by a complex number λ is to turn the vector z in an Argand diagram through the angle $\arg\lambda$ anticlockwise and stretch it by the scale factor $|\lambda|$ to give the vector λz.

In particular, if A, B, C represent the numbers a, b, c in an Argand diagram, then $\overrightarrow{BA}$ represents the complex number $a - b$, while $\overrightarrow{BC}$ represents $c - b$ (see figure 3.4). Therefore

$$\text{if} \quad \frac{a-b}{c-b} = \lambda \quad \text{then} \quad \text{angle ABC} = \arg \lambda = \arg\left(\frac{a-b}{c-b}\right).$$

Angle ABC here means the *anticlockwise* angle through which $\overrightarrow{BC}$ has to be turned to bring it into line with $\overrightarrow{BA}$.

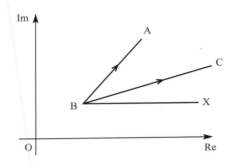

Figure 3.4

I ACTIVITY

Prove the same result by starting with $\arg\left(\dfrac{a-b}{c-b}\right) = \arg(a-b) - \arg(c-b)$.

EXAMPLE 3.10

Find the locus of points z for which $\arg\left(\dfrac{z-2j}{z+3}\right) = \dfrac{\pi}{3}$.

SOLUTION

Let A, B, P be the points representing $2j$, -3, z respectively.

The given condition shows that the direction of $\overrightarrow{AP}$ $(= z - 2j)$ is $\dfrac{\pi}{3}$ ahead of the direction of $\overrightarrow{BP}$ $(= z + 3)$, in the anticlockwise sense. Therefore $\angle APB = \dfrac{\pi}{3}$, and so (using the converse of the 'angles in the same segment' circle property) P lies on the arc of the circle with end points A and B as shown.

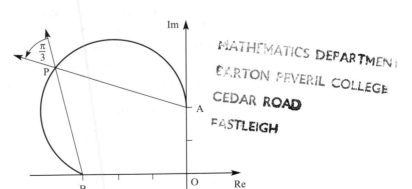

Figure 3.5

Find in a similar form the condition for P to lie on the other arc of this circle.

EXAMPLE 3.11

Two similar figures are *directly* similar if corresponding points moving round the two figures go in the same sense, either both clockwise or both anticlockwise. Find a condition for two triangles in an Argand diagram to be directly similar.

SOLUTION

Let A, B, C, D, E, F be the points representing a, b, c, d, e, f (see figure 3.6).

Then triangles ABC, DEF are directly similar if and only if

$$\frac{AB}{BC} = \frac{DE}{EF} \quad \text{and} \quad \text{angle ABC} = \text{angle DEF,}$$

both angles being in the same sense because the similarity is direct.

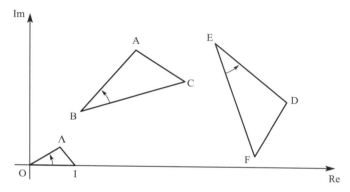

Figure 3.6

Therefore $\dfrac{|a-b|}{|c-b|} = \dfrac{|d-e|}{|f-e|}$ and $\arg\left(\dfrac{a-b}{c-b}\right) = \arg\left(\dfrac{d-e}{f-e}\right)$, and so $\dfrac{a-b}{c-b} = \dfrac{d-e}{f-e}$.

Note

The shape of these triangles is determined by the single complex number $\lambda = \dfrac{a-b}{c-b} = \dfrac{d-e}{f-e}$, and both triangles are similar to the triangle ΛOI with vertices λ, 0, 1 (see figure 3.6). When dealing with a set of similar triangles it can be helpful to make use of ΛOI as the 'standard representative' of the whole family of triangles with this shape.

ACTIVITY

Prove that the condition for two triangles ABC, DEF to have opposite similarity (where corresponding points move in opposite senses round the two triangles) is

$$\frac{a-b}{c-b} = \left(\frac{d-e}{f-e}\right)^\star.$$

EXAMPLE 3.12 Squares whose centres are P, Q, R are drawn outwards on the sides BC, CA, AB respectively of a triangle ABC. Prove that AP and QR are equal and mutually perpendicular.

SOLUTION

Working on an Argand diagram, let the points A, B, ... correspond to the complex numbers $a, b, \dots$ as usual (see figure 3.7).

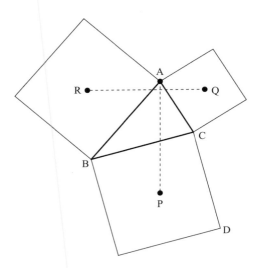

Figure 3.7

The first step is to find p in terms of b and c: two ways of doing this are given.

(i) If D is the vertex opposite B in the square with centre P then $\overrightarrow{CD}$ is obtained by turning $\overrightarrow{CB}$ through a right angle anticlockwise, and so $d - c = j(b - c)$. Therefore, since P is the mid-point of BD,

$$p = \frac{b + d}{2} = \frac{b + c + j(b - c)}{2}.$$

(ii) Alternatively, triangles BCP, CAQ, ABR are all right-angled isosceles triangles, and therefore all similar to the 'standard representative' triangle AOI with vertices $\frac{1 + j}{2}, 0, 1.$

Hence $\qquad \dfrac{p - c}{b - c} = \dfrac{q - a}{c - a} \overset{\bullet}{=} \dfrac{r - b}{a - b} = \dfrac{1 + j}{2},$

from which

$$p = c + \frac{(1 + j)(b - c)}{2} = \frac{b + c + j(b - c)}{2},$$

as before, and similarly

$$q = \frac{c + a + j(c - a)}{2} \quad \text{and} \quad r = \frac{a + b + j(a - b)}{2}.$$

It is now easy to complete the proof:

$$2(q-r) = c + a + j(c-a) - a - b - j(a-b)$$
$$= c - b + j(b+c) - 2ja$$
$$= j(b+c+j(b-c) - 2a)$$
$$= 2j(p-a).$$

Therefore $\overrightarrow{RQ}$ is obtained by turning $\overrightarrow{AP}$ through a right angle.

1 Explain the following construction for multiplication of given numbers z_1 and z_2 in an Argand diagram.

Draw the triangle with vertices $0, 1, z_1$. Then construct the directly similar triangle which has vertices 0 and z_2 corresponding to vertices 0 and 1 of the original triangle. The third vertex of the constructed triangle is z_1z_2.

Illustrate this by doing the construction for $z_1 = 2 + j$, $z_2 = 3 + 4j$. Then do the same with z_1 and z_2 interchanged.

2 Find the locus of points z for which

$$\arg\left(\frac{z-2j}{z+3}\right) = -\frac{\pi}{3}.$$

(Compare this with Example 3.10.)

3 On a single diagram draw and identify the locus of points z for which

$$\arg\left(\frac{z-3-2j}{z-1}\right) = \alpha \text{ where } \alpha \text{ is}$$

(i) $\dfrac{\pi}{4}$ **(ii)** $-\dfrac{\pi}{4}$ **(iii)** $\dfrac{3\pi}{4}$ **(iv)** $-\dfrac{3\pi}{4}$

4 Prove that $\arg\left(\dfrac{z-5}{z+5j}\right) = \dfrac{\pi}{4} \Rightarrow |z| = 5$.

Investigate whether the converse is true.

5 Given that $z_1 = 3 + 4j$, and $z_2 = -3 + 2j$, illustrate the following loci or regions on separate Argand diagrams. For parts **(i)** to **(v)** you are not required to give the cartesian equation of the loci.

(i) $|z - z_1| = 2$

(ii) $|z - z_2| \leqslant 2$

(iii) $0 \leqslant \arg(z - z_1) \leqslant \pi$ and $|z - z_1| \leqslant 1$

(iv) $|z - z_1| = |z - z_2|$

(v) $\arg(z - z_1) - \arg(z - z_2) = \dfrac{\pi}{2}$

(vi) Find the cartesian equation of the locus given by $|z - z_1| = 2|z - z_2|$ and draw a sketch to illustrate it.

[MEI]

6 Let A, B, C, D, E, F be the points representing a, b, c, d, e, f in an Argand diagram. Prove that triangles ABC, DEF are directly similar if and only if

$$ae + bf + cd = af + bd + ce.$$

Find in a similar form the condition for these triangles to have opposite similarity.

7 The points A, B, C in an Argand diagram represent the complex numbers a, b, c, and $a = (1 - \lambda)b + \lambda c$. Prove that if λ is real then A lies on BC and divides BC in the ratio $\lambda : 1 - \lambda$, but if λ is complex then, in triangle ABC, $AB : BC = |\lambda| : 1$ and angle $ABC = \arg \lambda$.

8 (i) If $\omega = \cos\dfrac{2\pi}{3} + j\sin\dfrac{2\pi}{3}$ and z is any vector, how are the vectors z and ωz related geometrically?

(ii) If $2 + 3j$ and $4 + 7j$ are two vertices of an equilateral triangle, find both possible positions for the third vertex.

9 (i) If the points a and b are two vertices of an equilateral triangle, prove that the third vertex is either $b + \omega(b - a)$ or $b + \omega^2(b - a)$, where ω is as in Question 8.

(ii) Show that these expressions can be written as $-\omega a - \omega^2 b$ and $-\omega^2 a - \omega b$ respectively.

(iii) Deduce that the triangle with vertices z_1, z_2, z_3 is equilateral if and only if

$$z_1 + \omega z_2 + \omega^2 z_3 = 0 \text{ or } z_1 + \omega^2 z_2 + \omega z_3 = 0.$$

(iv) Deduce that a necessary and sufficient condition for the points z_1, z_2, z_3 to form an equilateral triangle is

$$z_1^2 + z_2^2 + z_3^2 = z_2 z_3 + z_3 z_1 + z_1 z_2.$$

10 The points A, B, C in an Argand diagram represent the complex numbers a, b, c; M is the mid-point of AB, and G is the point dividing the median AM in the ratio $2:1$. Show that G represents the number $\dfrac{a + b + c}{3}$, and deduce from the symmetry of this expression that G also lies on the median through B and the median through C. (A *median* of a triangle is a line joining a vertex to the mid-point of the opposite side; the point G at which the medians meet is called the *centroid* of the triangle).

11 Directly similar triangles BCL, CAM, ABN are drawn on the sides of a triangle ABC. Prove that triangles ABC, LMN have the same centroid.

12 (i) On the sides of any triangle, equilateral triangles are drawn, pointing outward. Using Question 9 part **(ii)**, prove that the centroids of these equilateral triangles form another equilateral triangle. This is *Napoleon's theorem*; it was attributed to the Emperor within a few years of his death, and he was a good enough mathematician to have discovered it.

(ii) Prove that the theorem is still true if the equilateral triangles are drawn inward rather than outward.

(iii) Prove that the triangle of centroids in (i), the corresponding triangle in (ii), and the original triangle all have the same centroid.

13 (i) Squares whose centres are P, Q, R, S are drawn outwards on the sides AB, BC, CD, DA of a general quadrilateral ABCD. Prove that PR and QS are equal and mutually perpendicular.

(ii) What difference does it make if all the squares are drawn inwards?

(iii) Explain how the result of Example 3.12 can be deduced from (i).

INVESTIGATION

ROBERTS' THEOREM

Figure 3.8 shows four rods AB, BC, CD, DA which are flexibly linked. Rod AD is fixed (sometimes the points A and D are just fixed without being joined by a rod), and a triangle BCP is attached to rod BC.

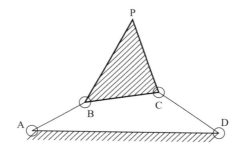

Figure 3.8

This mechanism is called a *four-bar linkage*: by adjusting the lengths of the rods and the shape of the triangle it is possible to achieve many different paths for the point P as the mechanism moves. Four-bar linkages are used to control the motion of parts of many machines (a good collection of examples is given in *Mathematics Meets Technology* by Brian Bolt, CUP, 1991). In 1878 the English engineer Richard Roberts proved that any motion of P which can be produced by a particular four-bar linkage can also be produced by two other linkages; this is useful since the other linkages may be more convenient to fit into the machine.

To prove Roberts' theorem you complete the parallelograms ABPE, DCPF, then construct triangles EPG, PFH directly similar to triangle BCP, and finally complete parallelogram GPHK (see figure 3.9).

Putting the figure on an Argand diagram, let $\overrightarrow{AB}$, $\overrightarrow{BC}$, $\overrightarrow{CD}$ represent the complex numbers u, v, w respectively, and let the shape of triangle BCP be defined by the complex number λ, so that $\overrightarrow{BP} = \lambda v$.

Copy figure 3.9 and mark on each edge the complex number it represents.

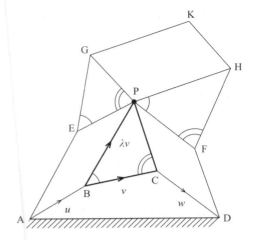

Figure 3.9

Deduce that $\overrightarrow{AK}$ represents $\lambda(u + v + w)$, and hence that K is a fixed point. This shows that the linkage AEGK with triangle EGP and linkage DFHK with triangle FHP also give the same motion for P.

1 de Moivre's theorem: $(\cos\theta + j\sin\theta)^n = \cos n\theta + j\sin n\theta$, where n is rational.

2 If $z = \cos\theta + j\sin\theta$ then

$$\frac{1}{z} = \cos\theta - j\sin\theta, \cos n\theta = \frac{z^n + z^{-n}}{2}, \sin n\theta = \frac{z^n - z^{-n}}{2j}.$$

3 $e^{j\theta} = \cos\theta + j\sin\theta, \quad \cos n\theta = \frac{e^{jn\theta} + e^{-jn\theta}}{2}, \quad \sin n\theta = \frac{e^{jn\theta} - e^{-jn\theta}}{2j}.$

4 The equation $z^n = 1$ has precisely n roots. These are

$$\omega^k = \cos\frac{2k\pi}{n} + j\sin\frac{2k\pi}{n}, \quad k = 0, 1, 2, ..., n-1.$$

The sum of all these nth roots of unity is zero.

5 The non-zero complex number $s(\cos\phi + j\sin\phi)$ has precisely n different nth roots. These are

$$s^{1/n}\left(\cos\left(\frac{\phi + 2k\pi}{n}\right) + j\sin\left(\frac{\phi + 2k\pi}{n}\right)\right), \quad \text{where } k = 0, 1, 2, ..., n-1.$$

The sum of these n roots is zero, and in an Argand diagram they are the vertices of a regular n-gon with centre O.

6 In an Argand diagram if $\frac{a - b}{c - b} = \lambda$ then

$$\text{angle ABC} = \arg\lambda = \arg\left(\frac{a - b}{c - b}\right),$$

and triangle ABC is similar to triangle ΛOI with vertices λ, 0, 1.

Calculus

The thought of the Differential Calculus warms my feet in bed.

Attributed to A.F. Pollard, 1869–1948

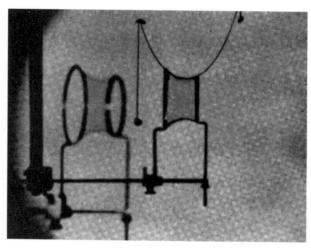

The soap bubble between two rings on the left casts a shadow which coincides with the hanging chain, showing that both form the same curve – a catenary.

The inverse trigonometric functions

The arcsine function

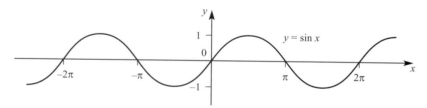

Figure 4.1

Figure 4.1 shows the graph of $y = \sin x$. The sine function is a many-to-one function: many values of x (for example: -2π, $-\pi$, 0, π, 2π, etc.) give the same value of y.

You can find the inverse of any function by interchanging x and y in the defining equation; this is equivalent to reflecting the graph in the line $y = x$. In the case of $y = \sin x$ you obtain the graph shown in figure 4.2; its equation is $x = \sin y$. For any value of x (between -1 and 1) there are infinitely many values of y, so figure 4.2 is not the graph of a function. However by restricting the range of y you can define a function, so that each value of x (between -1 and 1) is associated with a unique value of y. There are infinitely many ways of doing this, but it is conventional (and sensible) to include $0 \leqslant y \leqslant \frac{\pi}{2}$ (i.e. angles in the first quadrant) as part of the required range, corresponding to $0 \leqslant x \leqslant 1$.

To keep the function continuous (and to have as large a domain as possible) you include $-\frac{\pi}{2} \leqslant y < 0$, fourth quadrant angles, corresponding to $-1 \leqslant x < 0$. Figure 4.3 shows the complete graph of this function. Its equation is $y = \arcsin x$. (Older textbooks and many modern calculators use the notation $\sin^{-1}x$.) You will notice that the gradient of $y = \arcsin x$ is always positive, and that the gradient tends to infinity as $|x|$ tends to 1.

Now

$$y = \arcsin x$$
$$\Rightarrow \quad \sin y = x$$
$$\Rightarrow \quad \frac{dy}{dx} \cos y = 1$$
$$\Rightarrow \quad \frac{dy}{dx} = \frac{1}{\cos y}$$
$$= \frac{1}{\pm\sqrt{1 - \sin^2 y}}$$
$$= \frac{1}{\pm\sqrt{1 - x^2}}.$$

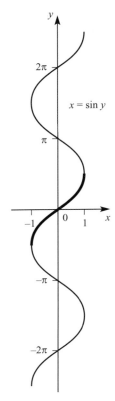

Figure 4.2

But $y = \arcsin x \Rightarrow -\frac{\pi}{2} \leqslant y \leqslant \frac{\pi}{2} \Rightarrow \cos y \geqslant 0$,

so that $\cos y = +\sqrt{1 - x^2}$. The conclusion is

that $\dfrac{d}{dx} (\arcsin x) = \dfrac{1}{\sqrt{1 - x^2}}$.

Notice that the expression $\dfrac{1}{\sqrt{1 - x^2}}$

• is positive and only defined for $-1 < x < 1$

• has a minimum at $x = 0$

• tends to ∞ as x tends to ±1

all of which is consistent with the graph in figure 4.3.

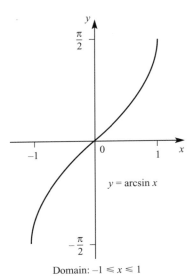

Domain: $-1 \leqslant x \leqslant 1$
Range: $-\frac{\pi}{2} \leqslant y \leqslant \frac{\pi}{2}$

Figure 4.3

The arccosine function

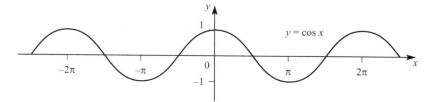

Figure 4.4

The inverse of the cosine function is dealt with in much the same way. Figure 4.4 shows the graph of $y = \cos x$. Reflecting the graph of figure 4.4 in the line $y = x$ produces the graph with equation $x = \cos y$, shown in figure 4.5. This is not the graph of a function. However, a function can be defined by restricting the range of y so that each value of x (between -1 and 1) is associated with a unique value of y. Again the values $0 \leqslant y \leqslant \frac{\pi}{2}$ are included (first quadrant angles), corresponding to $0 \leqslant x \leqslant 1$. To maximise the domain and preserve continuity, the range includes $\frac{\pi}{2} < y \leqslant \pi$, second quadrant angles. Figure 4.6 shows the complete graph of this function. Its equation is $y = \arccos x$.

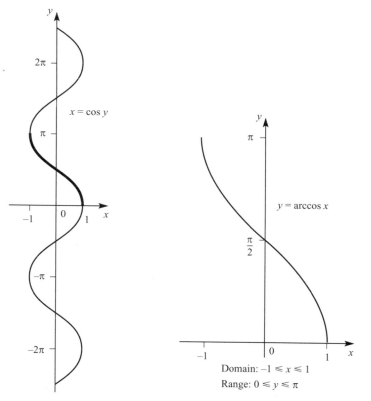

Figure 4.5   **Figure 4.6**

ACTIVITY

(i) From the various graphs (without using calculus) what can you say about the gradient of $y = \arccos x$?

(ii) Use calculus to show that $\dfrac{\mathrm{d}}{\mathrm{d}x}(\arccos x) = -\dfrac{1}{\sqrt{1-x^2}}$.

The arctangent function

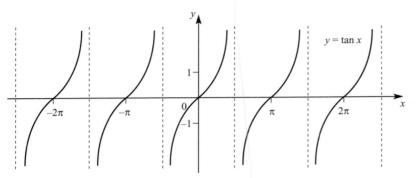

Figure 4.7

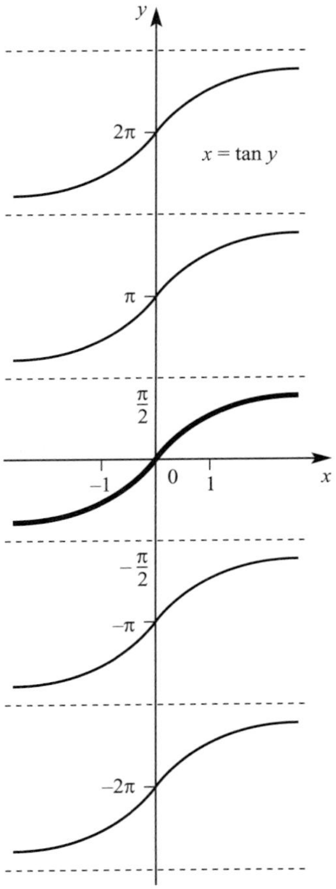

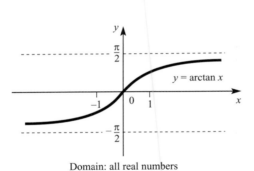

Domain: all real numbers

Range: $-\dfrac{\pi}{2} < y < \dfrac{\pi}{2}$

Figure 4.9

Figure 4.8

ACTIVITY

Describe the relationship of the various graphs shown in figures 4.7, 4.8 and 4.9.

Notice that the graph of $y = \arctan x$ has horizontal asymptotes. Describe qualitatively how its gradient varies and then use calculus methods to show that $\dfrac{\mathrm{d}}{\mathrm{d}x}(\arctan x) = \dfrac{1}{1+x^2}$.

The results $\dfrac{\mathrm{d}}{\mathrm{d}x}(\arcsin x) = \dfrac{1}{\sqrt{1-x^2}}$ and $\dfrac{\mathrm{d}}{\mathrm{d}x}(\arctan x) = \dfrac{1}{1+x^2}$ are particularly important, allowing you to integrate additional functions, as is shown in the next section.

Show that

(i) $\operatorname{arcsec} x \equiv \arccos\left(\dfrac{1}{x}\right)$

(ii) $\operatorname{arccosec} x \equiv \arcsin\left(\dfrac{1}{x}\right)$

(iii) $\operatorname{arccot} x \equiv \arctan\left(\dfrac{1}{x}\right)$ with $\operatorname{arccot} 0 = \dfrac{\pi}{2}$.

These formulae are useful as calculators, spreadsheets and other mathematical software frequently include only the three elementary trigonometric functions and their inverses.

General solutions

If you are looking for the *general solution* of an equation, you want a rule or formula which will give you all the solutions, but no other values (see *Pure Mathematics 3*, pages 56–57).

For example: one solution of the equation $\sin x = \frac{1}{2}$ is $x = \arcsin \frac{1}{2} = \dfrac{\pi}{6}$; another solution is $x = \pi - \dfrac{\pi}{6} = \dfrac{5\pi}{6}$; all solutions are in the first or second quadrants as $\sin x$ is positive. Every solution may be regarded as a number of complete rotations plus $\dfrac{\pi}{6}$ or $\dfrac{5\pi}{6}$.

These two forms of solution may be written as

$$x = 2m\pi + \frac{\pi}{6} \text{ or } (2m+1)\pi - \frac{\pi}{6}, \qquad \text{where } m \text{ is any integer.}$$

Alternatively you may combine these two expressions and write the general solution of $\sin x = \frac{1}{2}$ as $x = n\pi + (-1)^n \dfrac{\pi}{6}$, where n is any integer.

The table shows the other important forms.

Equation	Form of the general solution (n is any integer)
$\sin x = y$	$x = n\pi + (-1)^n \arcsin y$
$\cos x = y$	$x = 2n\pi \pm \arccos y$
$\tan x = y$	$x = n\pi + \arctan y$

1 State the domain and range of the inverse sine, cosine and tangent functions.

2 Show that $\arcsin x + \arccos x \equiv \dfrac{\pi}{2}$.

3 Show that $\arcsin(-x) = -\arcsin x$, and that $\arctan(-x) = -\arctan x$. State and prove a formula connecting $\arccos(-x)$ and $\arccos x$.

4 Show that $\arcsin(\sin \pi) \neq \pi$. Under what circumstances is $\arcsin(\sin x) = x$?

5 Show that $\arccos \sqrt{1-x} \equiv \arcsin \sqrt{x}$.

6 Differentiate the following with respect to x.

   (i) $\arcsin x$ **(ii)** $\arcsin 5x$

   (iii) $\arctan \dfrac{3x}{2}$ **(iv)** $\arctan(2-3x)$

7 Differentiate the following with respect to x.

   (i) $\arcsin 2x$ **(ii)** $\arctan 5x$

   (iii) $\arcsin 3x^2$ **(iv)** $\arccos 2x$

   (v) $\arctan(e^x)$ **(vi)** $\arctan(1-x^2)$

   (vii) $\arccos(5x^2-2)$ **(viii)** $\arcsin \sqrt{x}$

8 If $f(x) \equiv \sin x + \cos x$, $-\dfrac{\pi}{4} < x < \dfrac{\pi}{4}$, find $f^{-1}(x)$.

9 Write down the derivatives of $\arcsin x$ and $\arccos x$. Hence show that $\displaystyle\int \dfrac{1}{\sqrt{1-x^2}}\,dx$ may be expressed as $\arcsin x + c_1$ and as $-\arccos x + c_2$, where c_1 and c_2 are arbitrary constants. Explain how the two results are compatible, and express c_2 in terms of c_1.

10 In each of the following, find the general solution of the equation. Where possible give your answer as a rational multiple of π; otherwise leave your answer in a form involving an inverse trigonometric function.

   (i) $\sin 2x = \sin x$ **(ii)** $\cos x - \sin x = \sqrt{2}$

   (iii) $3\cos x + 4\sin x = 2.5$ **(iv)** $\tan 2x = 4\tan x$

   (v) $\cos x = \cos \frac{1}{2}x$ **(vi)** $2\sin x = \cos x + 1$

11 State the domain and range of

   (i) $y = \operatorname{arcsec} x$

   (ii) $y = \operatorname{arccosec} x$

   (iii) $y = \operatorname{arccot} x$.

12 (i) (a) By sketching the graph of $y = \operatorname{arcsec} x$ show that $\dfrac{d}{dx}(\operatorname{arcsec} x) > 0$.

      (b) Show that $\dfrac{d}{dx}(\operatorname{arcsec} x) = \dfrac{1}{|x|\sqrt{x^2-1}}$.

   (ii) Find

      (a) $\dfrac{d}{dx}(\operatorname{arccosec} x)$ **(b)** $\dfrac{d}{dx}(\operatorname{arccot} x)$.

13 Evaluate **(i)** $\operatorname{arcsec} x + \operatorname{arccosec} x$ **(ii)** $\arctan x + \operatorname{arccot} x$.

Integration using inverse trigonometric functions

The inverse sine and tangent functions are particularly useful in integration.

Integration using the arcsine function

Since $\dfrac{d}{dx}(\arcsin x) = \dfrac{1}{\sqrt{1-x^2}}$ you know that $\displaystyle\int \dfrac{1}{\sqrt{1-x^2}}\,dx = \arcsin x + c.$

You will see the similarity between $\displaystyle\int \dfrac{1}{\sqrt{9-x^2}}\,dx$ and $\displaystyle\int \dfrac{1}{\sqrt{1-x^2}}\,dx$ and you may well (correctly) guess that $\displaystyle\int \dfrac{1}{\sqrt{9-x^2}}\,dx$ takes a similar form, but you will perhaps be unsure what effect the number 9 has on the expression. Try treating 9 as a factor:

$$\int \frac{1}{\sqrt{9-x^2}}\,dx = \int \frac{1}{\sqrt{9\left(1-\dfrac{x^2}{9}\right)}}\,dx$$

$$= \int \frac{1}{3\sqrt{1-\left(\dfrac{x}{3}\right)^2}}\,dx \quad \text{Let } 3u = x \text{ so that } 3\,du = dx.$$

$$= \int \frac{1}{3\sqrt{1-u^2}} \times 3\,du$$

$$= \int \frac{1}{\sqrt{1-u^2}}\,du = \arcsin u + c = \arcsin\frac{x}{3} + c.$$

You can now construct the formula for $\displaystyle\int \dfrac{1}{\sqrt{a^2-x^2}}\,dx$, where a is a positive constant. As $x = 3u$ was a useful substitution when the denominator was $\sqrt{9-x^2}$, it makes sense to use the substitution $x = au$ so that $dx = a\,du$:

$$\int \frac{1}{\sqrt{a^2-x^2}}\,dx = \int \frac{1}{\sqrt{a^2-(au)^2}} \times a\,du$$

$$= \int \frac{1}{a\sqrt{1-u^2}} \times a\,du$$

$$= \int \frac{1}{\sqrt{1-u^2}}\,du = \arcsin u + c = \arcsin\frac{x}{a} + c.$$

EXAMPLE 4.1

Find **(i)** $\displaystyle\int \dfrac{1}{\sqrt{16-x^2}}\,dx$ **(ii)** $\displaystyle\int \dfrac{1}{\sqrt{16-3x^2}}\,dx.$

SOLUTION

(i) $\displaystyle\int \dfrac{1}{\sqrt{16-x^2}}\,dx = \arcsin\dfrac{x}{4} + c.$

> This is of the form $\displaystyle\int \dfrac{1}{\sqrt{a^2-x^2}}\,dx$ with $a = 4$.

(ii) $\displaystyle\int \dfrac{1}{\sqrt{16-3x^2}}\,dx = \dfrac{1}{\sqrt{3}}\int \dfrac{1}{\sqrt{\dfrac{16}{3}-x^2}}\,dx = \dfrac{1}{\sqrt{3}}\arcsin\dfrac{x\sqrt{3}}{4} + c.$

> Take out the factor $\sqrt{3}$, then as in **(i)** with $a = \dfrac{4}{\sqrt{3}}$.

Integration using the arctangent function

In the same way knowing that $\dfrac{d}{dx}(\arctan x) = \dfrac{1}{1 + x^2}$ so that

$\displaystyle\int \dfrac{1}{1 + x^2}\, dx = \arctan x + c$ may well lead you to guess that $\displaystyle\int \dfrac{1}{a^2 + x^2}\, dx$ takes a similar form. But

$$\int \dfrac{1}{a^2 + x^2}\, dx = \int \dfrac{1}{a^2 + a^2 u^2} \times a\, du \quad \text{putting } au = x \text{ so that } a\, du = dx$$

$$= \int \dfrac{1}{a(1 + u^2)}\, du \qquad \text{Notice the factor } \tfrac{1}{a}.$$

$$= \dfrac{1}{a} \arctan u + c = \dfrac{1}{a} \arctan \dfrac{x}{a} + c.$$

EXAMPLE 4.2   Find **(i)** $\displaystyle\int \dfrac{1}{5 + x^2}\, dx$ **(ii)** $\displaystyle\int \dfrac{1}{5 + 4x^2}\, dx.$

SOLUTION

(i) $\displaystyle\int \dfrac{1}{5 + x^2}\, dx = \dfrac{1}{\sqrt{5}} \arctan \dfrac{x}{\sqrt{5}} + c.$ This is of the form $\displaystyle\int \dfrac{1}{a^2 + x^2}\, dx$ with $a = \sqrt{5}$.

(ii) $\displaystyle\int \dfrac{1}{5 + 4x^2}\, dx = \dfrac{1}{4}\int \dfrac{1}{\frac{5}{4} + x^2}\, dx = \dfrac{1}{4} \times \dfrac{1}{\sqrt{\frac{5}{4}}} \arctan \dfrac{x}{\sqrt{\frac{5}{4}}} + c = \dfrac{1}{2\sqrt{5}} \arctan \dfrac{2x}{\sqrt{5}} + c.$

Take out the factor 4, then as in **(i)** with $a = \sqrt{\frac{5}{4}}$.

Note

Dimensions will help you understand (and remember) why the factor $\dfrac{1}{a}$ is needed in

$$\int \dfrac{1}{a^2 + x^2}\, dx = \dfrac{1}{a}\arctan \dfrac{x}{a} + c \qquad\qquad \text{①}$$

but not in

$$\int \dfrac{1}{\sqrt{a^2 - x^2}}\, dx = \arcsin \dfrac{x}{a} + c. \qquad\qquad \text{②}$$

Integration is a form of summation. In both integrals dx is a length. In ② the expression $\dfrac{1}{\sqrt{a^2 - x^2}}$ is a number divided by the square root of an area; multiplying by dx gives a dimensionless number; the sum of a series of numbers is dimensionless; $\arcsin \dfrac{x}{a}$ is an angle, also dimensionless $\left(\text{since an angle is a ratio of lengths} : \theta = \dfrac{s}{r}\right)$. So ② is dimensionally correct. In ① the expression $\dfrac{1}{a^2 + x^2}$ is a number divided by an area; multiplying by dx gives the dimension L^{-1} (i.e. the reciprocal of a length); summing these does not change the dimension; $\arctan \dfrac{x}{a}$ is dimensionless and multiplying it by something like $\dfrac{1}{a}$ (with the dimension L^{-1}) makes the two sides of ① agree dimensionally. (In ① the constant c has the dimension L^{-1}; in ② the constant c is dimensionless.)

The next example involves definite integration.

EXAMPLE 4.3

Evaluate $\displaystyle\int_0^2 \frac{1}{4 + x^2}\,dx$.

SOLUTION

Evaluate $\displaystyle\int_0^2 \frac{1}{4 + x^2}\,dx = \left[\frac{1}{2}\arctan\frac{x}{2}\right]_0^2 = \frac{1}{2}(\arctan 1 - \arctan 0) = \frac{\pi}{8}$.

ALTERNATIVE APPROACH

Alternatively you may make the substitution $x = 2\tan u$, remembering to change the limits of integration at the same time. But the equation $x = 2\tan u$ does not define u uniquely: given $x = 0$, for example, u may be 0, or π, or any multiple of π. However, though it looks more cumbersome, the equation $u = \arctan\dfrac{x}{2}$ does define u uniquely, and is the preferred way of stating the substitution. Then

$$\int_0^2 \frac{1}{4 + x^2}\,dx = \int_0^{\frac{\pi}{4}} \frac{2\sec^2 u}{4\sec^2 u}\,du \qquad \text{where } u = \arctan\frac{x}{2} \Rightarrow x = 2\tan u$$
$$\Rightarrow dx = 2\sec^2 u\,du;$$
$$= \int_0^{\frac{\pi}{4}} \frac{1}{2}\,du. \qquad \text{when } x = 2,\ u = \frac{\pi}{4};\ \text{when } x = 0,\ u = 0.$$
$$= \frac{1}{2}\left[u\right]_0^{\frac{\pi}{4}} = \frac{\pi}{8}.$$

EXERCISE 4B

1 Find the following indefinite integrals.

(i) $\displaystyle\int \frac{1}{25 + x^2}\,dx$

(ii) $\displaystyle\int \frac{1}{\sqrt{36 - x^2}}\,dx$

(iii) $\displaystyle\int \frac{5}{x^2 + 36}\,dx$

(iv) $\displaystyle\int \frac{4}{25 + 4x^2}\,dx$

(v) $\displaystyle\int \frac{1}{\sqrt{9 - 4x^2}}\,dx$

(vi) $\displaystyle\int \frac{7}{\sqrt{5 - 3x^2}}\,dx$

2 Evaluate the following definite integrals, leaving your answers in terms of π.

(i) $\displaystyle\int_0^3 \frac{1}{9 + x^2}\,dx$

(ii) $\displaystyle\int_0^{\sqrt{2}} \frac{1}{\sqrt{4 - x^2}}\,dx$

(iii) $\displaystyle\int_{-\frac{1}{\sqrt{3}}}^{\frac{1}{3}} \frac{1}{1 + 9x^2}\,dx$

(iv) $\displaystyle\int_0^{\frac{1}{4}} \frac{1}{\sqrt{1 - 4x^2}}\,dx$

(v) $\displaystyle\int_{-\frac{1}{2}}^{\frac{1}{2}} \frac{1}{\sqrt{3 - 6x^2}}\,dx$

(vi) $\displaystyle\int_{\sqrt{5/6}}^{\sqrt{5/2}} \frac{1}{5 + 2x^2}\,dx$

3 (i) Find $\displaystyle\int \frac{1}{9 + 16x^2}\,dx$.

(ii) Using the substitution $x = 2\sin\theta$, or otherwise, show that
$$\int_1^2 \sqrt{4 - x^2}\,dx = \frac{2\pi}{3} - \frac{\sqrt{3}}{2}.$$

[MEI, part]

Harder integrations

You have been integrating functions of the form: $\dfrac{1}{a^2 + x^2}$ and $\dfrac{1}{\sqrt{a^2 - x^2}}$.

The example below shows how the formula $\displaystyle\int \dfrac{1}{a^2 + x^2}\,dx = \dfrac{1}{a}\arctan\dfrac{x}{a} + c$ helps you integrate rational functions with constant numerator, and a denominator which is quadratic with no real roots.

EXAMPLE 4.4

Find $\displaystyle\int \dfrac{4}{x^2 - 2x + 3}\,dx.$

SOLUTION

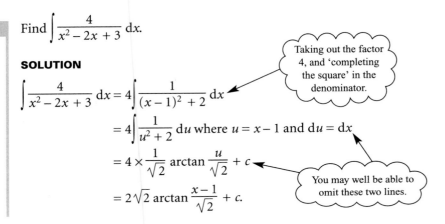

Taking out the factor 4, and 'completing the square' in the denominator.

$$\int \frac{4}{x^2 - 2x + 3}\,dx = 4\int \frac{1}{(x-1)^2 + 2}\,dx$$

$$= 4\int \frac{1}{u^2 + 2}\,du \text{ where } u = x - 1 \text{ and } du = dx$$

$$= 4 \times \frac{1}{\sqrt{2}}\arctan\frac{u}{\sqrt{2}} + c$$

$$= 2\sqrt{2}\arctan\frac{x-1}{\sqrt{2}} + c.$$

You may well be able to omit these two lines.

? When trying to integrate $\dfrac{1}{Ax^2 + Bx + C}$ how can you tell if $Ax^2 + Bx + C$ has no real roots? And what should you do if A is negative?

The next example shows how the formula $\displaystyle\int \dfrac{1}{\sqrt{a^2 - x^2}}\,dx = \arcsin\dfrac{x}{a} + c$ helps you integrate functions that can be arranged as a fraction, with constant numerator, and a denominator which is the square root of a quadratic; this quadratic must have distinct real roots and the coefficient of x^2 must be negative.

EXAMPLE 4.5

Find $\displaystyle\int \dfrac{5}{\sqrt{2 + 4x - 4x^2}}\,dx.$

Taking out the factor 5 from the numerator, and the factor 4 from 'inside' the square root in the denominator.

SOLUTION

$$\int \frac{5}{\sqrt{2 + 4x - 4x^2}}\,dx = \frac{5}{2}\int \frac{1}{\sqrt{\frac{1}{2} - (x^2 - x)}}\,dx$$

Completing the square first and the adjusting the constant to get $\frac{3}{4}$.

$$= \frac{5}{2}\int \frac{1}{\sqrt{\frac{3}{4} - \left(x - \frac{1}{2}\right)^2}}\,dx$$

$$= \frac{5}{2}\int \frac{1}{\sqrt{\frac{3}{4} - u^2}}\,du \text{ where } u = x - \frac{1}{2} \text{ and } du = dx$$

$$= \frac{5}{2}\arcsin\frac{2u}{\sqrt{3}} + c$$

Again you may well be able to omit these two lines.

$$= \frac{5}{2}\arcsin\frac{2x - 1}{\sqrt{3}} + c.$$

❓ When using the formula $\int \dfrac{1}{\sqrt{a^2 - x^2}} dx = \arcsin \dfrac{x}{a} + c$ to integrate $\dfrac{1}{\sqrt{Ax^2 + Bx + C}}$

why is it necessary to have A negative and $B^2 > 4AC$?

The final example illustrates other ways these techniques may be used.

EXAMPLE 4.6

Find **(i)** $\displaystyle\int \dfrac{x+5}{x^2+4} dx$ **(ii)** $\displaystyle\int \dfrac{x}{\sqrt{1-x^2}} dx$ **(iii)** $\displaystyle\int \dfrac{9x-8}{(x^2+9)(x+2)} dx$.

SOLUTION

(i) $\displaystyle\int \dfrac{x+5}{x^2+4} dx = \int \left(\dfrac{x}{x^2+4} + \dfrac{5}{x^2+4} \right) dx$

> The fraction being integrated is split into two parts: one numerator = constant × derivative of denominator; the other numerator is constant.

$$= \dfrac{1}{2} \int \dfrac{2x}{x^2+4} dx + 5 \int \dfrac{1}{x^2+4} dx$$

$$= \dfrac{1}{2} \ln(x^2+4) + 5 \times \dfrac{1}{2} \arctan \dfrac{x}{2} + c$$

$$= \dfrac{1}{2} \ln(x^2+4) + \dfrac{5}{2} \arctan \dfrac{x}{2} + c.$$

(ii) $\displaystyle\int \dfrac{x}{\sqrt{1-x^2}} dx$ is best found by inspection:

> Alternatively use any of the substitutions $u = \arcsin x$; $u = 1 - x^2$; $u^2 = 1 - x^2$.

$$\dfrac{d}{dx}(1-x^2)^{\frac{1}{2}} = \dfrac{1}{2}(1-x^2)^{-\frac{1}{2}} \times (-2x) = -\dfrac{x}{\sqrt{1-x^2}}$$

so that $\displaystyle\int \dfrac{x}{\sqrt{1-x^2}} dx = -\sqrt{1-x^2} + c.$

(iii) $\displaystyle\int \dfrac{9x-8}{(x^2+9)(x+2)} dx = \int \left(\dfrac{2x+5}{x^2+9} - \dfrac{2}{x+2} \right) dx$

> The rational function being integrated is expressed in partial fractions: see *Pure Mathematics 3*.

$$= \int \dfrac{2x+5}{x^2+9} dx - \int \dfrac{2}{x+2} dx$$

$$= \int \dfrac{2x}{x^2+9} dx + \int \dfrac{5}{x^2+9} dx - \int \dfrac{2}{x+2} dx$$

$$= \ln(x^2+9) + 5 \times \dfrac{1}{3} \arctan \dfrac{x}{3} - 2\ln|x+2| + c$$

$$= \ln \dfrac{x^2+9}{(x+2)^2} + \dfrac{5}{3} \arctan \dfrac{x}{3} + c.$$

> As $x^2 + 9$ and $(x+2)^2$ are clearly positive you do not need to use modulus signs here.

EXERCISE 4C

1 Find the following integrals.

(i) $\displaystyle\int \dfrac{1}{4+(x+2)^2} dx$

(ii) $\displaystyle\int \dfrac{7}{\sqrt{5+4x-x^2}} dx$

(iii) $\displaystyle\int \dfrac{3}{3+2x^2} dx$

(iv) $\displaystyle\int \dfrac{3}{9x^2+6x+5} dx$

(v) $\displaystyle\int \dfrac{1}{\sqrt{3+2x-x^2}} dx$

(vi) $\displaystyle\int \dfrac{7}{\sqrt{3-4x-4x^2}} dx$

2 (i) By writing $\arcsin x$ as $1 \times \arcsin x$ use integration by parts to find $\int \arcsin x \, dx$.

(ii) Use a similar method to find the following integrals.

(a) $\int \arccos x \, dx$

(b) $\int \arctan x \, dx$

(c) $\int \arccot x \, dx$

3 (i) Use the substitution $x = a \sin u$ to find

$$\int_0^b \sqrt{(a^2 - x^2)} \, dx, \text{ where } a > b > 0.$$

(ii) Draw a sketch to show the significance of the area you calculated in part **(i)**, and explain both terms of your answer to **(i)** geometrically.

4 Find the following integrals.

(i) $\displaystyle\int \frac{1}{x^2 - 6x + 13} \, dx$

(ii) $\displaystyle\int \frac{1}{\sqrt{7 - 12x - 4x^2}} \, dx$

(iii) $\displaystyle\int \frac{1}{4x^2 + 20x + 29} \, dx$

(iv) $\displaystyle\int \frac{1}{x^2 - 6x + 9} \, dx$

(v) $\displaystyle\int \frac{1}{\sqrt{5 - 12x - 9x^2}} \, dx$

5 Find the following integrals.

(i) $\displaystyle\int \frac{x+1}{x^2 + 1} \, dx$

(ii) $\displaystyle\int \frac{4}{(x^2 + 1)(1 + x)} \, dx$

(iii) $\displaystyle\int \frac{1-x}{\sqrt{1 - x^2}} \, dx$

(iv) $\displaystyle\int \frac{x+3}{(x+1)(x^2 + 1)} \, dx$

6 Evaluate the following:

(i) $\displaystyle\int_1^3 \frac{1}{\sqrt{4x - x^2}} \, dx$

(ii) $\displaystyle\int_2^5 \frac{2x^2 + 3}{(x-1)(x^2 + 4)} \, dx.$

7 Find $\dfrac{d}{dx} (\arcsec x)$ and $\displaystyle\int \frac{dx}{x\sqrt{x^2 - a^2}}.$

Hyperbolic functions

The hyperbolic cosine and hyperbolic sine functions

The cosine and sine functions are called *circular functions*, since the parametric equations $x = \cos\theta$, $y = \sin\theta$ give the circle $x^2 + y^2 = 1$. This equation can be rearranged to give $y = \pm \sqrt{1 - x^2}$, which is why the inverse circular functions are useful in finding integrals involving $\sqrt{1 - x^2}$ (and, likewise, $\sqrt{a^2 - x^2}$, as on page 70). In the eighteenth century several mathematicians investigated integrals involving $\sqrt{x^2 - 1}$ in a similar way, noticing that if $y = \sqrt{x^2 - 1}$ then $x^2 - y^2 = 1$ which is the equation of a hyperbola (as you will see on page 105).

Now $\qquad x^2 - y^2 = 1 \Longleftrightarrow (x + y)(x - y) = 1$

so that if $\qquad x + y = p$

then $\qquad x - y = \dfrac{1}{p}$

from which $\quad x = \dfrac{1}{2}\left(p + \dfrac{1}{p}\right)$ and $y = \dfrac{1}{2}\left(p - \dfrac{1}{p}\right).$

These are parametric equations for the hyperbola $x^2 - y^2 = 1$ in terms of the parameter p. (Compare Question 12 of Exercise 5C.)

These equations turn out to be particularly useful in the case when $p = e^u$, so that $\dfrac{1}{p} = e^{-u}$.

Then

$$x = \tfrac{1}{2}(e^u + e^{-u}) \quad \text{and} \quad y = \tfrac{1}{2}(e^u - e^{-u}).$$

By analogy with the circular functions these are called the *hyperbolic cosine* and *hyperbolic sine* functions respectively (names introduced by J. H. Lambert in 1768). These are abbreviated to *cosh* and *sinh* (pronounced 'shine' or 'sine–ch' or 'sinch' or 'sinsh' – take your pick!), so that

$$\cosh u = \tfrac{1}{2}(e^u + e^{-u}) \quad \text{and} \quad \sinh u = \tfrac{1}{2}(e^u - e^{-u}).$$

ACTIVITY

Prove that $\cosh(-u) = \cosh u$ and that $\sinh(-u) = -\sinh u$ (i.e. that cosh and sinh are respectively even and odd functions). What does this tell you about the symmetries of the graphs of these functions?

The graphs of these hyperbolic functions are easy to sketch. Since $\cosh u = \tfrac{1}{2}(e^u + e^{-u})$ the graph of $v = \cosh u$ lies mid-way between the graphs of $v = e^u$ and $v = e^{-u}$, as shown in figure 4.10. Note that $v = \cosh u$ has a minimum point at $(0, 1)$.

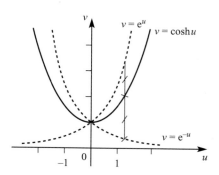

Figure 4.10

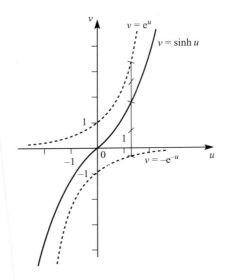

Figure 4.11

Similarly, the graph of $v = \sinh u$ is mid-way between the graphs of $v = e^u$ and $v = -e^{-u}$ (figure 4.11). It passes through the origin where it has a point of inflection.

These graphs are nothing like the sine or cosine wave graphs, but the definitions of the hyperbolic functions are very similar to the results linking the circular functions with $e^{j\theta}$ which were given on page 44. Compare

$$\cosh u = \frac{1}{2}(e^u + e^{-u}) \quad \text{and} \quad \cos\theta = \frac{1}{2}(e^{j\theta} + e^{-j\theta})$$

$$\sinh u = \frac{1}{2}(e^u - e^{-u}) \quad \text{and} \quad \sin\theta = \frac{1}{2j}(e^{j\theta} - e^{-j\theta}).$$

Many other similarities follow from this. For example, starting with the definitions and differentiating,

$$\frac{d}{du}(\cosh u) = \frac{1}{2}(e^u - e^{-u}) = \sinh u \quad \text{and} \quad \frac{d}{du}(\sinh u) = \frac{1}{2}(e^u + e^{-u}) = \cosh u.$$

Also, since $\cosh^2 u = \frac{1}{4}(e^u + e^{-u})^2 = \frac{1}{4}(e^{2u} + 2 + e^{-2u})$

and $\sinh^2 u = \frac{1}{4}(e^u + e^{-u})^2 = \frac{1}{4}(e^{2u} - 2 + e^{-2u})$

by subtracting

$$\cosh^2 u - \sinh^2 u = 1$$

and by adding

$$\cosh^2 u + \sinh^2 u = \frac{1}{2}(e^{2u} + e^{-2u}) = \cosh 2u.$$

> An important result, but not surprising since it gets us back to $x^2 - y^2 = 1$.

Using $\cosh^2 u - \sinh^2 u = 1$ and $\cosh 2u = \cosh^2 u + \sinh^2 u$, write down two further versions of $\cosh 2u$. Compare all three formulae for $\cosh 2u$ with the corresponding formulae for $\cos 2\theta$.

ACTIVITY

Use the definitions of sinh u and cosh u to prove that

(i) $\sinh 2u = 2\sinh u\cosh u$

(ii) $\sinh(u + v) = \sinh u\cosh v + \cosh u\sinh v$

(iii) $\cosh(u + v) = \cosh u\cosh v + \sinh u\sinh v$.

[**Hint:** Start with the right-hand sides.]

The only difference between these identities and the corresponding ones for the circular functions is that the sign is reversed whenever a product of two sines is replaced by the product of two sinhs. This is called Osborn's rule: it arises because of the factor j in the denominator of $\sin\theta$ as defined above.

EXAMPLE 4.7

Solve the equation $\cosh u = 2\sinh u - 1$.

SOLUTION

It is simplest to work from the definitions.

$$\cosh u = 2\sinh u - 1 \iff \tfrac{1}{2}(e^u + e^{-u}) = e^u - e^{-u} - 1$$
$$\iff e^u - 3e^{-u} - 2 = 0$$
$$\iff (e^u)^2 - 2e^u - 3 = 0$$
$$\iff (e^u - 3)(e^u + 1) = 0$$
$$\iff e^u = 3 \quad (\text{since } e^u \text{ cannot be negative})$$
$$\iff u = \ln 3.$$

EXERCISE 4D

1 Prove that

$$\cosh A + \cosh B = 2\cosh\frac{A + B}{2}\cosh\frac{A - B}{2}.$$

Write down the corresponding results for $\cosh A - \cosh B$ and for $\sinh A \pm \sinh B$, and prove one of these.

2 Given that $\sin 3\theta = 3\sin\theta - 4\sin^3\theta$ and $\cos 3\theta = 4\cos^3\theta - 3\cos\theta$, write down expressions for $\sinh 3u$ in terms of $\sinh u$ and $\cosh 3u$ in terms of $\cosh u$.

3 (i) Find all the real solutions of these equations.

(a) $\cosh x + 2\sinh x = -1$

(b) $10\cosh x - 2\sinh x = 11$

(c) $7\cosh x + 4\sinh x = 3$

(ii) Find conditions on a, b, c which are necessary and sufficient to ensure that the equation $a\cosh x + b\sinh x = c$ has two distinct real roots.

4 Given that $\sinh x + \sinh y = \frac{25}{12}$

and $\cosh x - \cosh y = \frac{5}{12}$,

show that $2e^x = 5 + 2e^{-y}$ and $3e^{-x} = -5 + 3e^y$.

Hence find the real values of x and y.

5 The figure below represents a cable hanging between two points A and B, where AB is horizontal. The lowest point of the cable, O, is taken as the origin of co-ordinates as shown.

If the cable is flexible and has uniform density then the curve in which it hangs is called a *catenary*. In 1691 John Bernoulli (responding to a challenge set by his brother James) proved that the equation of the catenary is $y = c\left(\cosh\frac{x}{c} - 1\right)$, where c is a constant [see *Pure Mathematics 6*, page 178].

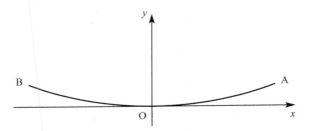

If for a particular cable $c = 20$ m and AB = 16 m, find the sag of the cable, i.e. the distance of O below AB, and the angle that the tangent at A makes with the horizontal.

6 P is any point on the curve $y = c\cosh\frac{x}{c}$, M is the foot of the perpendicular from P to the x axis, and Q is the foot of the perpendicular from M to the tangent of the curve at P. Prove that

(i) MQ = c

(ii) the product of the y co-ordinates of P and Q is c^2.

7 Differentiate each of the following with respect to x.

(i) $\sinh 4x$

(ii) $\cosh(x^2)$

(iii) $\cosh^2 x$

(iv) $\cos x \sinh x$

(v) $\sinh(\ln x)$

(vi) $e^{5x}\sinh 5x$

(vii) $(1 + x)^3\cosh^3 3x$

(viii) $\ln(\cosh x + \sinh x)$

8 Express $\cosh^2 x$ and $\sinh^2 x$ in terms of $\cosh 2x$.
Hence find $\int \cosh^2 x\, dx$ and $\int \sinh^2 x\, dx$.

9 Integrate each of the following with respect to x.

(i) $\sinh 3x$

(ii) $x\cosh(1 + x^2)$

(iii) $x\sinh x$

(iv) $\cosh^3 x$

(v) $x\sinh^2 x$

(vi) $e^{4x}\cosh 5x$

(vii) $\cosh^2 x \sinh^3 x$

(viii) $\cosh 6x \sinh 8x$

10 Prove that $\cosh x > x$ for all x. Prove that the point on the curve $y = \cosh x$ which is closest to the line $y = x$ has co-ordinates $(\ln(1 + \sqrt{2}), \sqrt{2})$.

11 Prove that $(\cosh x + \sinh x)^n = \cosh nx + \sinh nx$ for all integers n. State and prove the corresponding result for $(\cosh x - \sinh x)^n$. Deduce expressions for $\cosh 5x$ in terms of $\cosh x$ and for $\sinh 5x$ in terms of $\sinh x$.

12 In this question, the function $f(x)$ is defined to be

$$f(x) = 13 \cosh x + 5 \sinh x.$$

(i) For the curve with equation $y = f(x)$, show that the area under the curve between $x = -a$ and $x = a$ (where $a > 0$) is $\frac{13}{5}\{f(a) - f(-a)\}$.

(ii) By first expressing $f(x)$ in terms of e^x and e^{-x}, or otherwise, find the minimum value of $f(x)$.

(iii) Solve the equation $f(x) = 20$, giving the answers as natural logarithms.

(iv) Differentiate $\arctan\left(\frac{3}{2}e^x\right)$ with respect to x. Hence find $\displaystyle\int \frac{1}{f(x)} \, dx$.

[MEI]

Other hyperbolic functions

The four remaining hyperbolic functions are defined in a similar way to the corresponding circular functions:

$$\tanh x = \frac{\sinh x}{\cosh x}, \quad \coth x = \frac{1}{\tanh x}, \quad \operatorname{sech} x = \frac{1}{\cosh x}, \quad \operatorname{cosech} x = \frac{1}{\sinh x}.$$

ACTIVITY

For each of these functions state any necessary restriction on the domain, give the range, and say whether the function is even or odd.

The most important of these is the tanh function (pronounced 'than' or 'tan–ch').

Let $y = \tanh x$. Then $\quad y = \dfrac{e^x - e^{-x}}{e^x + e^{-x}} = \dfrac{1 - e^{-2x}}{1 + e^{-2x}} \quad$ ⟨dividing top and bottom by e^x⟩

so that $\quad y \to 1$ as $x \to \infty$.

By a similar method, $\quad y \to -1$ as $x \to -\infty$.

Using the quotient rule to differentiate $\dfrac{\sinh x}{\cosh x}$ gives

$$\frac{dy}{dx} = \frac{\cosh x \cosh x - \sinh x \sinh x}{\cosh^2 x} = \operatorname{sech}^2 x, \quad \text{since } \cosh^2 x - \sinh^2 x = 1.$$

So the graph of $y = \tanh x$ always has a positive gradient not exceeding 1 (since $0 < \operatorname{sech} x \leqslant 1$), has half-turn symmetry about the origin, and has asymptotes $y = \pm 1$ (see figure 4.12).

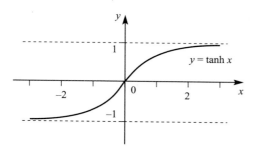

Figure 4.12

1 Sketch the graph of each of the following, giving the equations of any asymptotes.

    (i) $y = \operatorname{sech} x$

    (ii) $y = \operatorname{cosech} x$

    (iii) $y = \coth x$

2 Prove that

    (i) $1 - \tanh^2 x = \operatorname{sech}^2 x$

    (ii) $\coth^2 x - 1 = \operatorname{cosech}^2 x$

    (iii) $\tanh 2x = \dfrac{2 \tanh x}{1 + \tanh^2 x}$.

3 Find all the real solutions of these equations.

    (i) $4 \tanh x = \coth x$

    (ii) $3 \tanh x = 4(1 - \operatorname{sech} x)$

    (iii) $3 \operatorname{sech}^2 x + \tanh x = 3$

4 **(i)**   Find exact expressions for p and q, where $\sinh p = \operatorname{sech} p$ and $\cosh q = \coth q$.

    (ii)   Arrange $\cosh x$, $\sinh x$, $\tanh x$, $\operatorname{sech} x$, $\operatorname{cosech} x$, $\coth x$ in ascending order of magnitude

        (a)   when $0 < x < p$

        (b)   when $p < x < q$.

5 If $-\dfrac{\pi}{2} < x < \dfrac{\pi}{2}$ and k is any real constant, show that the equation $\sin x = \tanh k$ has just one solution, and prove that $\tan x = \sinh k$ and $\sec x = \cosh k$ for this value of x.

6 Prove that:

    (i) $\alpha = \ln(\tan \beta) \Longleftrightarrow \tanh \alpha = -\cos 2\beta$

    (ii) $\alpha = \ln\left(\tan\left(\dfrac{\pi}{4} + \dfrac{\beta}{2}\right)\right) \Longleftrightarrow \tanh \alpha = \sin \beta$.

7 Differentiate each of the following with respect to x.

    (i) $\operatorname{sech} x$ **(ii)** $\operatorname{cosech} x$

    (iii) $\coth x$ **(iv)** $\ln(\tanh x)$

8 Integrate each of the following with respect to x.

    (i) $\tanh x$ **(ii)** $\coth x$

    (iii) $\operatorname{sech} x$ **(iv)** $\operatorname{cosech} x$

[**Hint**: For **(iii)** and **(iv)** use the substitution $u = e^x$.]

The inverse hyperbolic functions

The cosh function is a many-to-one function, since more than one value of x can yield the same value of y (e.g. $\cosh x_1 = \cosh(-x_1) = y_1$ in figure 4.13).

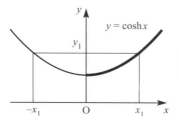

Figure 4.13

But if the domain is restricted to the non-negative real numbers, i.e. to $x \geqslant 0$, then the function is one-to-one, with the graph shown by the heavy line in figure 4.13. This restricted cosh function has an inverse function, which is denoted by *arcosh* (or sometimes $cosh^{-1}$), so that

$$v = \text{arcosh } u \qquad \Leftrightarrow \qquad u = \cosh v \text{ and } v \geqslant 0.$$

The usual process of reflecting the graph of a function in the line $y = x$ to give the graph of its inverse function produces the graph of $y = \text{arcosh } x$ shown in figure 4.14.

Since the sinh and tanh functions are already one-to-one there is no need for any similar restrictions in defining their inverse functions *arsinh* and *artanh* (or $sinh^{-1}$ and $tanh^{-1}$).

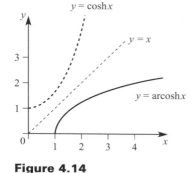

Figure 4.14

Thus
$$v = \text{arsinh } u \qquad \Leftrightarrow \qquad u = \sinh v$$
$$v = \text{artanh } u \qquad \Leftrightarrow \qquad u = \tanh v.$$

The graphs are shown in figure 4.15.

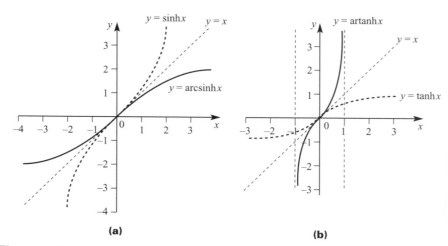

(a)   (b)

Figure 4.15

I ACTIVITY

State the domain and range of each of these three inverse hyperbolic functions.

Just as the hyperbolic functions are defined using the exponential function, so their inverses can be put in terms of the natural logarithm function. The most straightforward to deal with is artanh x:

$$y = \text{artanh } x \quad \Leftrightarrow \quad x = \tanh y$$

$$= \frac{e^y - e^{-y}}{e^y + e^{-y}}$$

$$= \frac{e^{2y} - 1}{e^{2y} + 1} \quad \text{(multiplying top and bottom by } e^y\text{)}$$

$$\Leftrightarrow \quad x(e^{2y} + 1) = e^{2y} - 1$$

$$\Leftrightarrow \quad e^{2y} = \frac{1 + x}{1 - x}$$

$$\Leftrightarrow \quad 2y = \ln\left(\frac{1 + x}{1 - x}\right).$$

Therefore artanh $x = \dfrac{1}{2} \ln\left(\dfrac{1 + x}{1 - x}\right)$.

As you might expect, arcosh x is a bit more complicated:

$$y = \text{arcosh } x \quad \Leftrightarrow \quad x = \cosh y$$

$$\Rightarrow \quad 2x = e^y + e^{-y}$$

$$\Rightarrow \quad (e^y)^2 - 2xe^y + 1 = 0$$

$$\Rightarrow \quad e^y = \frac{2x \pm \sqrt{4x^2 - 4}}{2} \quad \text{(using the quadratic equation formula)}$$

$$= x \pm \sqrt{x^2 - 1}$$

$$\Rightarrow \quad y = \ln(x + \sqrt{x^2 - 1}) \text{ or } \ln(x - \sqrt{x^2 - 1}).$$

The sum of these two roots is

$$\ln\left[x + \sqrt{x^2 - 1}\right)\left(x - \sqrt{x^2 - 1}\right] = \ln\left[x^2 - (x^2 - 1)\right] = \ln 1 = 0,$$

so the second root is the negative of the first (as shown in figure 4.13). Since arcosh $x > 0$ by definition, the required root is the positive one. Therefore arcosh $x = \ln(x + \sqrt{x^2 - 1})$.

ACTIVITY

Use a similar method to prove that arsinh $x = \ln(x + \sqrt{x^2 + 1})$.

Explain why the root $\ln(x - \sqrt{x^2 + 1})$ is rejected.

The derivatives of arcosh x and arsinh x can be found by differentiating these logarithmic versions, but it is easier to work as follows.

$$y = \text{arcosh } x \quad \Leftrightarrow \quad \cosh y = x$$

$$\Rightarrow \quad \sinh y \frac{dy}{dx} = 1 \quad \text{(differentiating both sides with respect to } x\text{)}$$

$$\Rightarrow \quad \frac{dy}{dx} = \frac{1}{\sinh y}$$

$$= \frac{1}{\pm\sqrt{\cosh^2 y - 1}} \quad \text{(using } \cosh^2 y - \sinh^2 y = 1\text{)}$$

$$= \frac{1}{\pm\sqrt{x^2 - 1}}.$$

Since the gradient of $y = \operatorname{arcosh} x$ is always positive you must take the positive square root, and therefore $\dfrac{d}{dx}(\operatorname{arcosh} x) = \dfrac{1}{\sqrt{x^2 - 1}}$.

This result is equivalent to the integral $\displaystyle\int \dfrac{1}{\sqrt{x^2 - 1}}\, dx = \operatorname{arcosh} x + c$, from which it is easy to integrate related functions. For example, to find $\displaystyle\int \dfrac{1}{\sqrt{x^2 - a^2}}\, dx$, use the substitution $x = au$. Then $dx = a\, du$ and

$$\int \frac{1}{\sqrt{x^2 - a^2}}\, dx = \int \frac{1}{\sqrt{a^2 u^2 - a^2}}\, a\, du$$

$$= \int \frac{1}{a\sqrt{u^2 - 1}}\, a\, du$$

$$= \int \frac{1}{\sqrt{u^2 - 1}}\, du$$

$$= \operatorname{arcosh} u + c$$

$$= \operatorname{arcosh} \frac{x}{a} + c.$$

ACTIVITY

Prove by similar methods that

(i) $\dfrac{d}{dx}(\operatorname{arsinh} x) = \dfrac{1}{\sqrt{x^2 + 1}}$

(ii) $\displaystyle\int \dfrac{1}{\sqrt{x^2 + a^2}}\, dx = \operatorname{arsinh} \dfrac{x}{a} + c.$

Inverse hyperbolic functions are used in integration in much the same way as inverse trigonometric functions. More complicated examples use techniques such as taking out constant factors or completing the square, just as on pages 73–74.

EXAMPLE 4.8

Find

(i) $\displaystyle\int \dfrac{1}{\sqrt{9x^2 - 25}}\, dx$

(ii) $\displaystyle\int \sqrt{x^2 - 1}\, dx$

(iii) $\displaystyle\int_{1}^{5} \dfrac{1}{\sqrt{x^2 + 6x + 13}}\, dx.$

SOLUTION

(i) $\displaystyle\int \dfrac{1}{\sqrt{9x^2 - 25}}\, dx = \dfrac{1}{3}\int \dfrac{1}{\sqrt{x^2 - \dfrac{25}{9}}}\, dx$

$$= \frac{1}{3} \operatorname{arcosh} \frac{3x}{5} + c.$$

(ii) Let $x = \cosh u$ so that $\mathrm{d}x = \sinh u\, \mathrm{d}u$. Then

$$\int \sqrt{x^2 - 1}\, \mathrm{d}x = \int \sqrt{\cosh^2 u - 1}\, \sinh u\, \mathrm{d}u$$

$$= \int \sinh^2 u\, \mathrm{d}u$$

$$= \int \tfrac{1}{2}(\cosh 2u - 1)\, \mathrm{d}u$$

$$= \tfrac{1}{4}\sinh 2u - \tfrac{1}{2}u + c$$

$$= \tfrac{1}{2}\sinh u \cosh u - \tfrac{1}{2}u + c$$

$$= \tfrac{1}{2}x\sqrt{x^2 - 1} - \tfrac{1}{2}\operatorname{arcosh} x + c.$$

(iii) $x^2 + 6x + 13 = x^2 + 6x + 9 + 4 = (x + 3)^2 + 4.$

Therefore $\displaystyle\int_1^5 \frac{1}{\sqrt{x^2 + 6x + 13}}\, \mathrm{d}x = \int_1^5 \frac{1}{\sqrt{(x + 3)^2 + 4}}\, \mathrm{d}x$

$$= \left[\operatorname{arsinh} \frac{x + 3}{2}\right]_1^5$$

$$= \operatorname{arsinh} 4 - \operatorname{arsinh} 2$$

$$= \ln(4 + \sqrt{17}) - \ln(2 + \sqrt{5})$$

$$\approx 0.651.$$

1 Differentiate $\ln(x + \sqrt{x^2 - 1})$ with respect to x, and show that your answer simplifies to $\dfrac{1}{\sqrt{x^2 - 1}}$.

2 Prove that $\dfrac{\mathrm{d}}{\mathrm{d}x}(\operatorname{artanh} x) = \dfrac{1}{1 - x^2}$. By using partial fractions and integrating, deduce from this the logarithmic form of $\operatorname{artanh} x$.

3 Sketch the graphs of the inverse functions $y = \operatorname{arsech} x$, $y = \operatorname{arcosech} x$, $y = \operatorname{arcoth} x$, giving the domain and range of each.

4 Differentiate each of the following with respect to x.

    (i) $\operatorname{arsinh} 3x$

    (ii) $\operatorname{arcosh}(x^2)$

    (iii) $\arctan(\sinh x)$

    (iv) $\operatorname{artanh}(\sin x)$

    (v) $\operatorname{arsech} x$

5 Integrate the following with respect to x.

    (i) $\operatorname{arcosh} x$

    (ii) $\operatorname{arsinh} x$

    (iii) $\operatorname{artanh} x$.

[**Hint:** Write $\operatorname{arcosh} x = 1 \times \operatorname{arcosh} x$ and integrate by parts.]

6 Integrate the following with respect to x.

(i) $\dfrac{1}{\sqrt{4+x^2}}$

(ii) $\dfrac{1}{\sqrt{x^2-9}}$

(iii) $\dfrac{1}{\sqrt{9-x^2}}$

(iv) $\dfrac{1}{\sqrt{36x^2+16}}$

(v) $\dfrac{1}{\sqrt{x^2-4x+8}}$

(vi) $\dfrac{1}{\sqrt{x^2+x}}$

(vii) $\dfrac{1}{\sqrt{9x^2+6x-8}}$

(viii) $\dfrac{x^2}{\sqrt{x^6-1}}$

7 Evaluate each of the following, correct to 3 significant figures.

(i) $\displaystyle\int_1^3 \dfrac{1}{\sqrt{x^2+4x+5}}\,dx$

(ii) $\displaystyle\int_{10}^{20} \dfrac{1}{\sqrt{4x^2+12x-40}}\,dx.$

8 The points $P_1(a\cos\theta, a\sin\theta)$ and $P_2(a\cosh\phi, a\sinh\phi)$ lie on the circle $x^2+y^2=a^2$ and the rectangular hyperbola $x^2-y^2=a^2$ respectively (see diagram below).

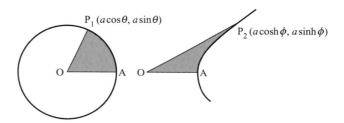

Prove that area OAP_1 is proportional to θ and that area OAP_2 is proportional to ϕ, with the same constant of proportionality.

9 By substituting suitable circular or hyperbolic functions, find

(i) $\displaystyle\int \sqrt{a^2-x^2}\,dx$

(ii) $\displaystyle\int \sqrt{a^2+x^2}\,dx$

(iii) $\displaystyle\int \sqrt{x^2-a^2}\,dx.$

10 Show that $\displaystyle\int_5^6 \dfrac{1}{\sqrt{25x^2-576}}\,dx = \dfrac{1}{5}\ln\!\left(\dfrac{3}{2}\right).$

[MEI, part]

11 Show that $\displaystyle\int_0^4 \dfrac{4x+1}{\sqrt{x^2+9}}\,dx = 8+\ln 3.$

[MEI, part]

12 (i) Find $\displaystyle\int x\sinh(x^2)\,dx.$

(ii) By writing $x^3\sinh(x^2)$ as $x^2(x\sinh(x^2))$, or otherwise, find $\displaystyle\int x^3\sinh(x^2)\,dx.$

[MEI, part]

13 (i) Find the exact value of $\int_{-0.4}^{0.4} \dfrac{1}{25x^2 + 4}\, dx$.

(ii) (a) Differentiate the following with respect to x (where $0 < x < 2$), simplifying your answers as much as possible.

    (A) $\arcsin\dfrac{x}{2}$ (B) $\operatorname{arcosh}\dfrac{2}{x}$

(b) Using integration by parts, show that

$$\int_{0}^{\sqrt{3}} \arcsin\frac{x}{2}\, dx = \frac{\pi}{\sqrt{3}} - 1.$$

(c) Find $\displaystyle\int \dfrac{2 + 3x}{x\sqrt{4 - x^2}}\, dx$.

[MEI]

14 (i) Obtain the formula

$$\sinh 2x - \sinh 2y = 2\cosh(x + y)\sinh(x - y)$$

and prove that

$$\cosh\theta + \cosh 2\theta + \cdots + \cosh n\theta = \cosh\tfrac{1}{2}(n + 1)\theta \sinh\tfrac{1}{2}n\theta \operatorname{cosech}\tfrac{1}{2}\theta.$$

(ii) Evaluate the integral

$$\int_{\frac{3}{2}}^{\frac{7}{2}} \frac{dx}{\sqrt{4x^2 - 4x - 3}}.$$

[MEI]

15 Prove that the curves $y = \operatorname{arsinh} x$ and $y = \operatorname{arcosh} 2x$ intersect where

$$x = \frac{1}{\sqrt{3}}.$$

Find the area bounded by the x axis and these curves.

4

Calculus

1 Inverse trigonometric functions

Function	Domain	Range	Derivative
$y = \arcsin x$	$-1 \leqslant x \leqslant 1$	$-\dfrac{\pi}{2} \leqslant y \leqslant \dfrac{\pi}{2}$	$\dfrac{1}{\sqrt{1-x^2}}$
$y = \arccos x$	$-1 \leqslant x \leqslant 1$	$0 \leqslant y \leqslant \pi$	$-\dfrac{1}{\sqrt{1-x^2}}$
$y = \arctan x$	all x	$-\dfrac{\pi}{2} < y < \dfrac{\pi}{2}$	$\dfrac{1}{1+x^2}$

2 $\displaystyle\int \frac{1}{a^2+x^2}\,dx = \frac{1}{a}\arctan\frac{x}{a} + c$

Use when integrating rational functions with constant numerator, and a quadratic denominator with no real roots.

3 $\displaystyle\int \frac{1}{\sqrt{a^2-x^2}}\,dx = \arcsin\frac{x}{a} + c$

Use when integrating functions that can be arranged as a fraction, with constant numerator, and a denominator which is the square root of a quadratic; this quadratic must have distinct real roots, and the coefficient of x^2 must be negative.

4 $\cosh x = \dfrac{e^x + e^{-x}}{2}$, $\sinh x = \dfrac{e^x - e^{-x}}{2}$, $\tanh x = \dfrac{\sinh x}{\cosh x} = \dfrac{e^{2x}-1}{e^{2x}+1}$,

$\coth x = \dfrac{1}{\tanh x}$, $\operatorname{sech} x = \dfrac{1}{\cosh x}$, $\operatorname{cosech} x = \dfrac{1}{\sinh x}$.

5 $\cosh^2 x - \sinh^2 x = 1$, $\quad 1 - \tanh^2 x = \operatorname{sech}^2 x$, $\quad \coth^2 x - 1 = \operatorname{cosech}^2 x$.

6 $\cosh(x \pm y) = \cosh x \cosh y \pm \sinh x \sinh y$,

$\sinh(x \pm y) = \sinh x \cosh y \pm \cosh x \sinh y$,

$\tanh(x \pm y) = \dfrac{\tanh x \pm \tanh y}{1 \pm \tanh x \tanh y}$.

7 $\dfrac{d}{dx}(\cosh x) = \sinh x$, $\dfrac{d}{dx}(\sinh x) = \cosh x$, $\dfrac{d}{dx}(\tanh x) = \operatorname{sech}^2 x$,

$\displaystyle\int \cosh x\,dx = \sinh x + c$, $\displaystyle\int \sinh x\,dx = \cosh x + c$, $\displaystyle\int \tanh x\,dx = \ln(\cosh x) + c$.

8 $\operatorname{arcosh} x = \ln(x + \sqrt{x^2-1})$, $\operatorname{arsinh} x = \ln(x + \sqrt{x^2+1})$, $\operatorname{artanh} x = \frac{1}{2}\ln\left(\dfrac{1+x}{1-x}\right)$.

9 $\displaystyle\int \frac{1}{\sqrt{x^2-a^2}}\,dx = \operatorname{arcosh}\frac{x}{a} + c$, $\displaystyle\int \frac{1}{\sqrt{x^2+a^2}}\,dx = \operatorname{arsinh}\frac{x}{a} + c$.

5 Conics 1

Undoubtedly the record for the pay-back of a mathematical theory is held by the humble ellipse. Studied by the Greeks it really came into its own when planetary orbits were fully understood more than 1000 years later.

Sir Michael Atiyah, President of the Royal Society, 1994

Each cable in the main span of a suspension bridge forms a parabola

The family of curves called *conics* takes a central place in mathematics, having a long history, a rich geometry, and many important applications. You have already met some members of the family: parabolas, ellipses and hyperbolas (see *Pure Mathematics 1* pages 92–93, *Pure Mathematics 3* pages 106–107 and page 75 of this book). This chapter aims to make you familiar with some of the many properties of these individual curves. Then Chapter 7 brings together their common features and shows how these originate in the sections of a cone.

Historical note

The Greek mathematician Apollonius of Perga (c.262–190 BC) wrote an eight-volume study of conics, building on earlier work. The astronomer Johannes Kepler gave conics new importance when he announced in 1609 that the orbits of the planets are ellipses, and in *The Two New Sciences* (1638) Galileo Galilei showed that the path of a projectile is a parabola.

The parabola

A *parabola* is defined as the locus of a point in a plane such that its distance from a fixed point S equals its distance from a fixed straight line d, both S and d being in the plane.

The fixed point S is called the *focus*, and the fixed line d is called the *directrix*.

ACTIVITY

On squared paper draw a set of parallel vertical lines 1 cm apart, and label one of these d. Mark a grid point S 2 cm from d. Draw circles with centre S and radii 1, 2, 3, … cm. Mark the points of intersection of the circle with radius r cm and the line r cm from d. Hence draw the parabola with focus S and directrix d.

The line through S perpendicular to d is called the *axis* of the parabola. If this axis meets the directrix at A then the mid-point O of AS is equidistant from S and d. Therefore O is a point of the parabola; O is called the *vertex* of the parabola. By convention, diagrams are drawn with the directrix vertical, the axis horizontal, and O and S to the right of A, as in figure 5.1.

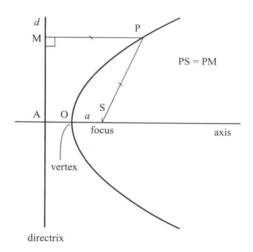

Figure 5.1

The standard cartesian equation uses the axis of the parabola as the x axis, with the origin at the vertex O. Then if OS = a the focus S is $(a, 0)$ and the directrix d is $x = -a$ (see figure 5.2).

The point P(x, y) is on the parabola $\iff$ SP = PM (by definition)
$\iff$ SP^2 = PM^2
$\iff$ $(x - a)^2 + y^2 = (x + a)^2$
$\iff$ $y^2 = (x + a)^2 - (x - a)^2$
$\iff$ $y^2 = 4ax$.

This is the cartesian equation of the parabola in its standard form.

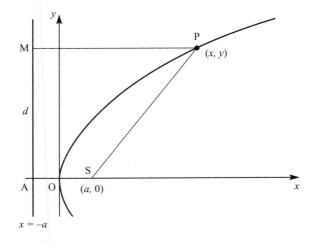

Figure 5.2

The distance a determines the size of the parabola, but all parabolas are the same shape. In particular taking $a = \frac{1}{4}$ and then interchanging the x and y axes shows that the familiar curve with equation $y = x^2$ is a parabola with focus $\left(0, \frac{1}{4}\right)$.

The parabola $y^2 = 4ax$ has simple parametric equations. Take (x, y) as any point on this parabola, and let $t = \frac{y}{2a}$; then $x = \frac{y^2}{4a} = \frac{4a^2t^2}{4a} = at^2$. So the parabola has parametric equations $x = at^2$, $y = 2at$, and all the points of the parabola can be given in the form $(at^2, 2at)$, with a unique value of t for each point.

ACTIVITY

Choose a convenient size for a and mark on a diagram the position of $(at^2, 2at)$ for $t = -3, -2, -1, -\frac{1}{2}, 0, \frac{1}{2}, 1, 2, 3$. Notice how the point moves along the parabola as t increases. If t changes at a constant rate does the point move with constant speed?

EXAMPLE 5.1

The points T and U of the parabola $y^2 = 4ax$ have co-ordinates $(at^2, 2at)$ and $(au^2, 2au)$ respectively. Find the equation of

(i) the chord TU

(ii) the tangent to the parabola at T

(iii) the normal to the parabola at T.

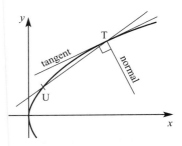

Figure 5.3

SOLUTION

(i) The gradient of TU is

$$\frac{2at-2au}{at^2-au^2} = \frac{2(t-u)}{t^2-u^2} = \frac{2}{t+u}.$$

The line through T with this gradient has the equation

$$y-2at = \frac{2}{t+u}(x-at^2)$$

$$\Leftrightarrow \quad (t+u)y - 2at(t+u) = 2x - 2at^2$$

$$\Leftrightarrow \quad 2x - (t+u)y + 2atu = 0.$$

(Note that this is symmetrical in t and u, as the geometry demands.)

(ii) The tangent at T is the limiting position of the chord TU as $U \rightarrow T$ along the curve, i.e. as $u \rightarrow t$. Letting $u \rightarrow t$ in the equation of the chord (and cancelling the common factor 2) gives the equation of the tangent:

$$x - ty + at^2 = 0.$$

(iii) From **(ii)** the gradient of the tangent at T is $\frac{1}{t}$, so the gradient of the normal is $-t$. The equation of the normal is

$$y - 2at = -t(x - at^2)$$

$$\Leftrightarrow \quad tx + y - 2at - at^3 = 0.$$

ACTIVITY

Prove these results about the gradient of the tangent and the equation of the tangent again, using calculus.

A *focal chord* is a chord which passes through the focus.

ACTIVITY

Prove that TU is a focal chord if and only if $tu = -1$.

EXAMPLE 5.2

Prove that the tangents at the ends of a focal chord meet at right angles on the directrix.

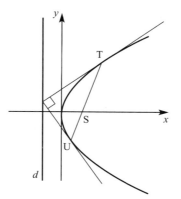

Figure 5.4

SOLUTION

From the previous two activities the gradients of the tangents at T and U are $\dfrac{1}{t}$ and $\dfrac{1}{u}$, and $tu = -1$. Therefore the product of the gradients is -1, and so the tangents are perpendicular.

The equations of the tangents are

$$x - ty + at^2 = 0,$$ ①
$$x - uy + au^2 = 0.$$ ②

Taking ① × u – ② × t to eliminate y gives

$$(u - t)x + at^2u - au^2t = 0$$

⟺ $$(u - t)x = atu(u - t)$$

⟺ $$x = atu$$

$$= -a \text{ since } tu = -1.$$

> rearranging and factorising

> Cancelling $(u - t)$, which is not zero since T and U are distinct.

Therefore the tangents meet on the directrix.

*Throughout this exercise **P** is the parabola with cartesian equation $y^2 = 4ax$.*

1 The diagram shows a double square STUVU′T′ together with O, the mid-point of SV. Prove that the parabola with focus S and directrix UVU′ passes through T, O and T′, and touches VT and VT′. (Sketching or imagining this double square helps to give a reasonably correct shape when sketching a parabola.)

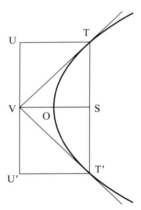

2 Draw a quick sketch of each of these parabolas, giving the co-ordinates of the vertex and focus, and the equations of the axis and directrix.

(i) $y^2 = 12x$

(ii) $y^2 = -x$

(iii) $(y - 2)^2 = 4(x - 3)$

(iv) $6y = x^2$

(v) $y^2 + 10y = 8x - 9$

(vi) $2y + x^2 + 6x - 1 = 0$

3 Find the equation of the parabola

(i) with focus $(5, 7)$ and directrix $x = -3$

(ii) with vertex $(-4, 2)$ and directrix $x = 6$

(iii) with vertex $(4, -1)$ and focus $(4, 7)$.

4 The point P of *P* has co-ordinates $(at^2, 2at)$; S is the focus, and M is the foot of the perpendicular from P to the directrix. The tangent at P meets SM at Z. Draw a diagram and prove that

(i) PZ is the perpendicular bisector of SM

(ii) Z is on the tangent at O

(iii) PZ bisects angle SPM.

5 Take a rectangular sheet of paper and mark a point S about 4 cm from the left-hand edge and about half-way down the sheet. Fold the paper so that this edge passes through S, make a sharp crease, and then unfold the paper. Do this repeatedly, always using the same edge but changing the position of the crease slightly each time. Use Question 4 part **(i)** to prove that all these creases touch a parabola, and identify its focus and directrix.

6 Draw a straight line *m* and a point S not on it. Place a set square with the right angle on *m* and one arm of the right angle through S. Draw the *other* arm of the right angle. Do this repeatedly, moving the right angle slightly along *m* each time but always keeping one arm through S. When necessary turn the set square over and move the right angle in the other direction along *m*. Use Question 4 part **(ii)** to prove that all these lines touch a parabola, and identify its focus and vertex.

7 A parabola has parametric equations $x = at^2$, $y = 2at$.

(i) Find the equation of the tangent to the parabola at the point $P(ap^2, 2ap)$.

The tangents to the parabola at the points $P(ap^2, 2ap)$ and $Q(aq^2, 2aq)$, where $p \neq q$, meet at the point T.

(ii) Show that the co-ordinates of T are $(apq, a(p + q))$.

The mid-point of PQ is M, and the mid-point of TM is R.

(iii) Show that TM is parallel to the *x* axis.

(iv) Show that R lies on the parabola.

(v) Show that the tangent to the parabola at R is parallel to PQ.

[MEI]

8 The tangent to the parabola $y^2 = 4ax$ at the point $P(ap^2, 2ap)$ meets the directrix at R, and S is the focus.

(i) Find the co-ordinates of R.

(ii) Prove that PS is perpendicular to RS.

9 The parametric equations of a parabola are $x = at^2$, $y = 2at$. P and Q are two points on this parabola with parameters t_1 and t_2 respectively.

(i) **(a)** Derive the equation of the chord PQ.

(b) P and Q now vary in such a way that line PQ has a fixed gradient. Show that $t_1 + t_2$ is constant.

(c) Write down the co-ordinates of the mid-point of PQ. Show that the mid-points of chords of a parabola which are in a fixed direction, lie on a line parallel to its axis.

(ii) (a) Find the equation of the tangent to the parabola at R(aT^2, $2aT$).

(b) Show that this tangent will also be a tangent to the circle

$$x^2 + y^2 = \tfrac{1}{2}a^2 \text{ if } 2T^4 - T^2 - 1 = 0.$$

(c) Find the equations of the two real common tangents to the circle and the parabola.

[MEI]

10 P, Q, R, P′, Q′, R′ are points on *P* such that PQ′ is parallel to P′Q and QR′ is parallel to Q′R. Prove that RP′ is parallel to R′P.

[**Hint:** Write down conditions in terms of the parameters of these points for the given chords to be parallel.]

11 Prove that a circle which has a focal chord of a parabola as diameter touches the directrix.

12 The tangent and normal at a point P of *P* meet the axis at T and G respectively, and N is the foot of the perpendicular from P to the axis. Prove that TN is bisected by the vertex, and that NG is constant.

13 A parabola has equation $y^2 = 4ax$.

(i) Find the equation of the normal to the parabola at the point (at^2, $2at$).

(ii) Show that the normal to the parabola at the point (a, $-2a$) passes through the point ($15a$, $12a$).

(iii) The normals at two other points on the parabola also pass through the point ($15a$, $12a$).
Find the co-ordinates of these two points.

[MEI, part]

14 If the normal to *P* at (at^2, $2at$) meets *P* again at (au^2, $2au$), show that $t^2 + tu + 2 = 0$, and deduce that u^2 cannot be less than 8.

The line $3y = 2x + 4a$ meets *P* at the points H and K. Prove that the normals at H and K meet on *P*.

The ellipse

There are several ways of defining an ellipse, so one of the challenges, to be taken up in Chapter 7, is to prove that these all lead to the same curve. The following definition has the advantage of immediately giving a simple practical method for drawing ellipses.

An *ellipse* is the locus of a point P in a plane such that the sum of the distances of P from two fixed points S, S′ in the plane is constant (see figure 5.5).

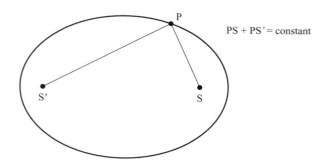

Figure 5.5

Each fixed point, S or S′, is called a *focus* of the ellipse. An ellipse can be drawn by passing a loop of thread around fixed pins at S and S′, and drawing this taut with a pencil pressed against the paper. As the pencil moves, keeping the string taut, it draws an ellipse.

ACTIVITY

Draw some ellipses by this method. Notice the effect of changing the separation SS′ without changing the length of the loop.

It is immediately clear from the definition that the ellipse is a closed curve which is symmetrical about both SS′ and the perpendicular bisector of SS′. With the notation of figure 5.6, AA′ is called the *major axis*, and BB′ is the *minor axis*. These meet at the *centre* O. Any chord through O is called a *diameter*, and is bisected at O.

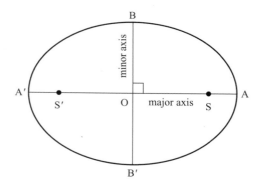

Figure 5.6

If OA = a then for any point P of the ellipse

$$SP + S'P = SA + S'A \qquad \text{using the definition}$$
$$= S'A' + S'A \qquad \text{since } SA = S'A' \text{ by symmetry}$$
$$= AA'$$
$$= 2a,$$

so that the constant length in the definition equals the length of the major axis.

You have seen in the activity above that altering the separation SS' produces different ellipses even when the major axis is kept fixed. The shape of an ellipse depends on how far each focus is from the centre, measured as a fraction of a. This fraction $\dfrac{OS}{OA}$ is called the *eccentricity* (from the Latin for *from the centre*) and is denoted by e (nothing to do with 2.718...).

(i) How does the shape of an ellipse change as e increases from 0 to 1?

(ii) What 'ellipses' are obtained when $e = 0$ and when $e = 1$?

(iii) Why is it impossible to have an ellipse with $e > 1$?

In figure 5.7, since B is on the ellipse and is equidistant from S and S', BS = BS' = a. Therefore if OB = b then, applying Pythagoras to the right-angled triangle OSB,

$$b^2 + a^2e^2 = a^2$$

which can be rearranged as

$$b^2 = a^2(1 - e^2) \quad \text{or} \quad e^2 = \frac{a^2 - b^2}{a^2}.$$

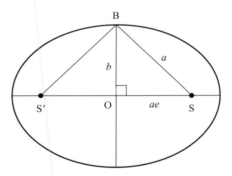

Figure 5.7

(i) Find the eccentricity of an ellipse with axes of lengths
  (a) 10 cm, 6 cm
  (b) 50 cm, 48 cm
  (c) 1 m, 1 cm.

(ii) An ellipse has eccentricity $\frac{2}{3}$. Find, to the nearest centimetre,
  (a) b when $a = 100$ cm
  (b) a when $b = 100$ cm.

The focus–directrix property

To use co-ordinates it is best to take the major and minor axes as x and y axes respectively, so that S and S' are $(\pm ae, 0)$. Let P(x, y) be a point of the ellipse with PS = r and PS' = r' (see figure 5.8).

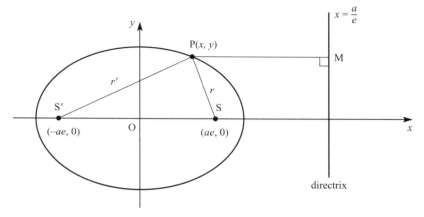

Figure 5.8

Applying the distance formula for co-ordinates,

$$r^2 = (x - ae)^2 + y^2, \qquad r'^2 = (x + ae)^2 + y^2.$$

Therefore $\qquad\qquad\qquad r^2 - r'^2 = (x - ae)^2 - (x + ae)^2 = -4aex.$

But $\qquad\qquad\qquad r^2 - r'^2 = (r + r')(r - r') = 2a(2r - 2a)$ since $r' = 2a - r$.

So $\qquad\qquad\qquad 2a(2r - 2a) = -4aex$

which simplifies to $\qquad\qquad r - a = -ex$

from which $\qquad\qquad\qquad r = a - ex,$

which can be written as $\qquad r = e\left(\dfrac{a}{e} - x\right).$ ①

Now $\left(\dfrac{a}{e} - x\right)$ is the distance PM of P from the line $x = \dfrac{a}{e}$. This line is called the *directrix* corresponding to the focus S, and ① shows that the distance from P to S is e times the distance from P to this directrix. Thus the ellipse has the property PS = ePM, where $e < 1$ (compare this with the defining property of a parabola, PS = PM, given on page 90).

The cartesian equation

Finding the cartesian equation is now straightforward.

The point P(x, y) is on the ellipse $\quad\Longleftrightarrow\quad$ SP = ePM

$\qquad\qquad\qquad\qquad\qquad\qquad\quad\Longleftrightarrow\quad$ SP^2 = e^2PM^2

$\qquad\qquad\qquad\qquad\qquad\qquad\quad\Longleftrightarrow\quad (x - ae)^2 + y^2 = e^2\left(\dfrac{a}{e} - x\right)^2$

$\qquad\Longleftrightarrow\quad x^2 - 2aex + a^2e^2 + y^2 = a^2 - 2aex + e^2x^2$

$\qquad\Longleftrightarrow\quad x^2(1 - e^2) + y^2 = a^2(1 - e^2)$

$\qquad\Longleftrightarrow\quad \dfrac{x^2}{a^2} + \dfrac{y^2}{a^2(1 - e^2)} = 1$

$\qquad\Longleftrightarrow\quad \dfrac{x^2}{a^2} + \dfrac{y^2}{b^2} = 1$, since $b^2 = a^2(1 - e^2)$.

This is the standard cartesian equation of the ellipse, which you have already met in *Pure Mathematics 3*, page 106. By symmetry in the y axis there is a second focus S' at $(-ae, 0)$, and corresponding to this a second directrix d' with equation $x = -\dfrac{a}{e}$ (see figure 5.9).

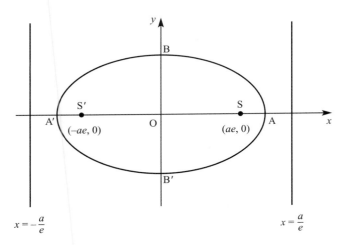

Figure 5.9

Another way of obtaining an ellipse is by squashing a circle. To be more precise, consider the one-way stretch with matrix $\begin{pmatrix} 1 & 0 \\ 0 & b/a \end{pmatrix}$. This maps the point (X, Y) to the point (x, y) where $\begin{pmatrix} x \\ y \end{pmatrix} = \begin{pmatrix} 1 & 0 \\ 0 & b/a \end{pmatrix}\begin{pmatrix} X \\ Y \end{pmatrix} = \begin{pmatrix} X \\ bY/a \end{pmatrix}$, so that the x co-ordinate is unchanged, and the y co-ordinate is multiplied by b/a (which gives a 'squash' rather than a 'stretch' since $b/a < 1$):

$$x = X, \qquad y = \frac{bY}{a} \qquad \text{or } Y = \frac{ay}{b}.$$

Now apply this transformation to the circle with centre O and radius a (figure 5.10).

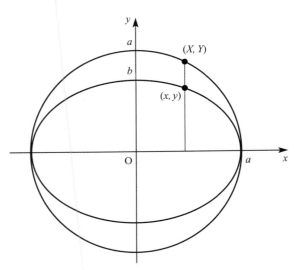

Figure 5.10

(X, Y) is on this circle $\Leftrightarrow X^2 + Y^2 = a^2$

$$\Leftrightarrow x^2 + \frac{a^2 y^2}{b^2} = a^2$$

$$\Leftrightarrow \frac{x^2}{a^2} + \frac{y^2}{b^2} = 1$$

$\Leftrightarrow (x, y)$ is on the ellipse.

This shows that an ellipse is formed by shortening, in a given ratio, all the chords of a circle which are perpendicular to one diameter. When you look at a circular object you often see an ellipse because of your oblique viewpoint.

| ACTIVITY

Find the determinant of $\begin{pmatrix} 1 & 0 \\ 0 & b/a \end{pmatrix}$. Deduce that the area of the ellipse is πab.

This 'squashing' transformation leads to the very useful standard parametric equations for the ellipse. If P_1 is the point on the circle with centre O and radius a such that angle $AOP_1 = \theta$ then P_1 has co-ordinates $(a\cos\theta, a\sin\theta)$ and the corresponding point P on the ellipse has co-ordinates $\left(a\cos\theta, \frac{b}{a} \times a\sin\theta\right)$,

i.e. $(a\cos\theta, b\sin\theta)$.

So the ellipse has parametric equations $x = a\cos\theta$, $y = b\sin\theta$ (see figure 5.11).

As θ increases from 0 to 2π the point P moves once round the ellipse. The angle θ is called the *eccentric angle* of the point P; notice that this is *not* the angle AOP.

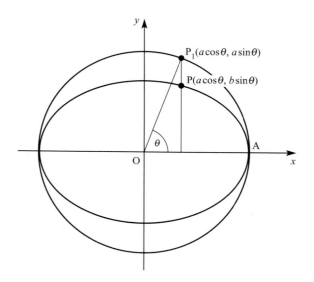

Figure 5.11

EXAMPLE 5.3

Find the equation of **(i)** the tangent **(ii)** the normal to the standard ellipse at $P(a\cos\theta, b\sin\theta)$.

SOLUTION

(i) $x = a\cos\theta \Rightarrow \dfrac{dx}{d\theta} = -a\sin\theta$ and $y = b\sin\theta \Rightarrow \dfrac{dy}{d\theta} = b\cos\theta$.

Therefore $\dfrac{dy}{dx} = -\dfrac{b\cos\theta}{a\sin\theta}$ and the equation of the tangent at P is

$$y - b\sin\theta = -\frac{b\cos\theta}{a\sin\theta}(x - a\cos\theta)$$

$$\Leftrightarrow \quad ay\sin\theta - ab\sin^2\theta = -bx\cos\theta + ab\cos^2\theta$$

$$\Leftrightarrow \quad bx\cos\theta + ay\sin\theta = ab(\cos^2\theta + \sin^2\theta)$$

$$\Leftrightarrow \quad \frac{x\cos\theta}{a} + \frac{y\sin\theta}{b} = 1.$$

(ii) Using $mm' = -1$ for perpendicular lines the gradient of the normal is $\dfrac{a\sin\theta}{b\cos\theta}$.

The equation of the normal at P is

$$y - b\sin\theta = \frac{a\sin\theta}{b\cos\theta}(x - a\cos\theta)$$

$$\Leftrightarrow \quad by\cos\theta - b^2\cos\theta\sin\theta = ax\sin\theta - a^2\cos\theta\sin\theta$$

$$\Leftrightarrow \quad ax\sin\theta - by\cos\theta = (a^2 - b^2)\cos\theta\sin\theta.$$

EXERCISE 5B

Throughout this exercise E is the ellipse with cartesian equation $\dfrac{x^2}{a^2} + \dfrac{y^2}{b^2} = 1$.

1 Draw the ellipse $\dfrac{x^2}{25} + \dfrac{y^2}{16} = 1$ accurately on graph paper. Calculate the eccentricity, and add the foci and directrices to your diagram. Check the properties $SP = ePM$ and $S'P = ePM'$ by measurement from your diagram for three positions of the point P on this ellipse.
Note: *foci, directrices* are the plurals of *focus, directrix.*)

2 The orbit of the planet Pluto is an ellipse with major axis of length 1.18×10^{10} km and eccentricity $\frac{1}{4}$. Calculate the length of the minor axis.

3 Rearrange $2(x - 1)^2 + 11(y - 4)^2 = 22$ in the form $\dfrac{(x - h)^2}{a^2} + \dfrac{(y - k)^2}{b^2} = 1$.
Hence show that this is the equation of an ellipse.
Find the co-ordinates of the centre and the foci, the equations of the directrices, and sketch the ellipse.

4 Repeat Question 3 for the equation $x^2 + 2y^2 + 4x - 8y + 4 = 0$.

5 Find the equations of the tangent and normal to the ellipse $\dfrac{x^2}{6} + \dfrac{y^2}{3} = 1$ at the point (2, 1). Prove that the line $y = x + 3$ also touches this ellipse, and find the point of contact.

6 Prove that the ratio of the least and greatest distances of a point of **E** from a focus is $1 - e : 1 + e$.

7 The orbit of Halley's comet is an ellipse with the sun at one focus. The distances of the perihelion and the aphelion from the sun are 0.587 a.u. and 17.947 a.u. respectively. Find the eccentricity of the orbit.
(The *perihelion* and *aphelion* are the points of an orbit closest to and furthest from the sun; the *astronomical unit* (a.u.) is the mean distance of the earth from the sun, about 1.5×10^{11} m.)

8 The orbit of a satellite is an ellipse of eccentricity $\frac{1}{35}$ with the centre of the earth at one focus. The earth may be treated as a sphere of radius 6400 km. If the least height of the satellite above the earth's surface is 400 km, what is the greatest height?

9 Explain why the distance d from the centre of the sun to the earth is inversely proportional to the angle α which the sun's diameter subtends at a point of the earth (see below).

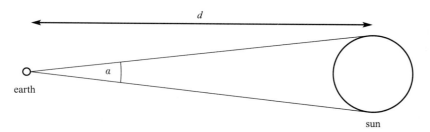

At the perihelion of the earth's orbit this angle is 32'36" and at the aphelion it is 31'32". Calculate the eccentricity of the earth's orbit. (The *minute* (') and *second* (") are used to measure small angles: $1° = 60'$, $1' = 60"$.)

10 The *elliptic trammel* is a mechanical device for drawing ellipses.

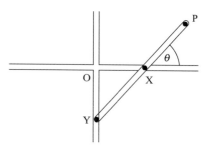

It consists of a straight rod with a pencil at P and pegs at X, Y which run in perpendicular grooves OX, OY. Prove that if OX, OY are taken as x and y axes with PX = b, PY = a, then the locus of P is *E*.

(**Hint**: Use the angle θ shown in the diagram.)

11 A ladder slides in a fixed vertical plane with its foot on the horizontal floor and its top against a vertical wall. A pot of paint is hooked onto the ladder, not at either end. Prove that the locus of the pot is part of an ellipse. Where is the pot if this ellipse is a circle?

12 The line $y = mx + c$ meets the ellipse $\dfrac{x^2}{a^2} + \dfrac{y^2}{b^2} = 1$ at two points P and Q.

  (i) Show that the x co-ordinates of P and Q satisfy

$$(a^2m^2 + b^2)x^2 + (2a^2mc)x + a^2(c^2 - b^2) = 0.$$

  (ii) Find the co-ordinates of the mid-point of PQ (in terms of a, b, m and c).

  (iii) Show that the mid-point of PQ lies on the line $y = -\dfrac{b^2}{a^2m}\, x$.

  Now suppose that P is the point $(a\cos\theta,\ b\sin\theta)$ and PQ is the normal to the ellipse at P.

  (iv) Find the gradient of PQ in terms of a, b and θ.

  (v) Given that the mid-point of PQ lies on the line $y = -x$, show that $\tan\theta = \dfrac{b^3}{a^3}$.

                                                                             [MEI]

13 **(i)** Show that the x co-ordinates of the points of intersection of the line $y = mx + c$ and the ellipse $\dfrac{x^2}{a^2} + \dfrac{y^2}{b^2} = 1$ (where $a > b > 0$) satisfy the quadratic equation $(a^2m^2 + b^2)x^2 + (2a^2mc)x + a^2(c^2 - b^2) = 0$.

  (ii) Deduce that if $y = mx + c$ is a tangent to the ellipse, then $c^2 = a^2m^2 + b^2$, and show that the point of contact is $\left(-\dfrac{a^2m}{c}, \dfrac{b^2}{c}\right)$.

  A tangent passing through the point $(0, a)$ touches the ellipse at P and meets the x axis at Q.

  (iii) Show that Q lies on a directrix of the ellipse.

  (iv) Show that the foot of the perpendicular from P to the x axis is a focus of the ellipse.

                                                                           [MEI]

14 Use Question 13 part **(ii)** to show that the tangents from the point $(-2, 5)$ to the ellipse $\dfrac{x^2}{6} + \dfrac{y^2}{3} = 1$ have gradients -1 and 11. Find the equations of these two tangents. Find also the co-ordinates of the point of contact of each tangent.

15 **(i)** Use Question 13 part **(ii)** to prove that the gradients of the two tangents from the point (X, Y) to E are the roots of the quadratic equation

$$m^2(a^2 - X^2) + 2mXY + b^2 - Y^2 = 0.$$

  (ii) Find the condition for this equation to have complex roots, and interpret this geometrically.

  (iii) Find the condition for the product of the roots to equal -1. Deduce that the tangents from the point (X, Y) to E are perpendicular if and only if (X, Y) lies on the circle $x^2 + y^2 = a^2 + b^2$. (This is called the *director circle* of the ellipse.)

  (iv) An elliptical disc slides between two fixed perpendicular lines. Prove that the locus of its centre is an arc of a circle.

16 The point P of E has co-ordinates $(a\cos\theta, b\sin\theta)$. The normal at P meets the x axis at N, and the foot of the perpendicular from the origin O to the tangent at P is M. Prove that $OM \times PN = b^2$.

17 **Conjugate diameters**

If the eccentric angles of points P and U of E differ by $\pm\dfrac{\pi}{2}$ then the diameters PQ and UV are called *conjugate* diameters.

(i) Prove that when a circle is 'squashed' to form an ellipse (as on page 99), perpendicular diameters of the circle become conjugate diameters of the ellipse.

(ii) Prove that if conjugate diameters of E have gradients m, m' then $mm' = -\dfrac{b^2}{a^2}$.

(iii) Prove that, for conjugate diameters PQ and UV, $PQ^2 + UV^2 = 4(a^2 + b^2)$.

(iv) Prove that the locus of the mid-points of chords of E which are parallel to a diameter PQ is the conjugate diameter.

[**Hint:** 'Unsquash' the ellipse back to a circle, noting that under this transformation mid-points of lines remain mid-points.]

(v) Prove that the area of the parallelogram formed by the four tangents at the ends of a pair of conjugate diameters is always $4ab$.

(vi) PQ is a diameter and R is any other point of an ellipse. Prove that the diameters parallel to PR and QR are conjugate.

(vii) A parallelogram is inscribed in an ellipse. Prove that its sides are parallel to a pair of conjugate diameters. Deduce that just one square can be inscribed in E, and prove that its area is $\dfrac{4a^2b^2}{a^2 + b^2}$.

The hyperbola

Both the conics studied so far have the focus–directrix property $PS = ePM$ (using the notation of pages 90 and 98), where $0 < e < 1$ for an ellipse and $e = 1$ for a parabola. The natural extension of this when $e > 1$ gives the definition of a hyperbola.

> A *hyperbola* is the locus of a point P in a plane such that its distance from a fixed point S is a constant e times its distance from a fixed line d, where S and d are in the plane and $e > 1$.

As before, S is called a focus and d is the corresponding directrix.

The hyperbola is clearly symmetrical about the line through S perpendicular to d; this line is called the *transverse axis*. Let X be the point where the directrix meets the transverse axis. The hyperbola meets the transverse axis at two points, A and A' say, which are the points dividing XS internally and externally in the ratio $1 : e$.

The cartesian equation

Now let O be the mid-point of AA', and take O as the origin of cartesian co-ordinates, with the transverse axis as x axis (see figure 5.12).

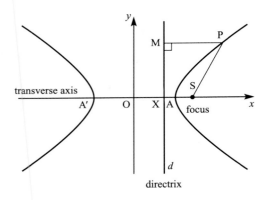

Figure 5.12

Let OS = h and OX = k. Then using the focus–directrix definition for the points A and A' gives

$$SA = eAX, \quad \text{i.e. } h - a = e(a - k),$$
$$SA' = eA'X, \quad \text{i.e. } h + a = e(a + k),$$

from which $h = ae$ and $k = \dfrac{a}{e}$. Thus the focus S is $(ae, 0)$ and the directrix d is $x = \dfrac{a}{e}$.

The point P(x, y) is on the hyperbola $\iff$ SP = ePM

$$\iff \quad SP^2 = e^2PM^2$$
$$\iff \quad (x - ae)^2 + y^2 = e^2\left(x - \frac{a}{e}\right)^2$$
$$\iff \quad x^2 - 2aex + a^2e^2 + y^2 = e^2x^2 - 2aex + a^2$$
$$\iff \quad x^2(1 - e^2) + y^2 = a^2(1 - e^2)$$
$$\iff \quad \frac{x^2}{a^2} + \frac{y^2}{a^2(1 - e^2)} = 1$$
$$\iff \quad \frac{x^2}{a^2} - \frac{y^2}{a^2(e^2 - 1)} = 1$$
$$\iff \quad \frac{x^2}{a^2} - \frac{y^2}{b^2} = 1, \text{ where } b^2 = a^2(e^2 - 1).$$

> It is convenient to change signs here since $a^2(e^2 - 1)$ is positive.

This is the standard cartesian equation of the hyperbola.

The y axis (which the curve does not meet) is called the *conjugate axis*. Since the equation contains only even powers of x and y the hyperbola is symmetrical about both axes, so there are two foci, at $(\pm ae, 0)$, and two directrices with equations $x = \pm \dfrac{a}{e}$ (see figure 5.13). Notice that the directrices are closer to the origin than the foci, since $e > 1$.

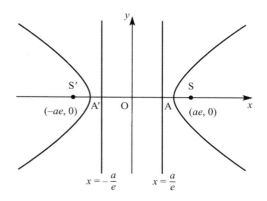

Figure 5.13

For many purposes the most convenient parametric equations for the hyperbola are

$$x = a\sec\theta, \quad y = b\tan\theta.$$

ACTIVITY

Check that $(a\sec\theta, b\tan\theta)$ satisfies $\dfrac{x^2}{a^2} - \dfrac{y^2}{b^2} = 1$. Describe how this point moves once along the whole hyperbola as θ increases from 0 to 2π, paying particular attention to what happens when θ is near $\dfrac{\pi}{2}$ or $\dfrac{3\pi}{2}$.

ACTIVITY

Prove that, for points $(a\sec\theta, b\tan\theta)$ of the hyperbola, $\dfrac{y}{x} \to \dfrac{b}{a}$ as $\theta \to \dfrac{\pi}{2}$ and $\dfrac{y}{x} \to -\dfrac{b}{a}$ as $\theta \to \dfrac{3\pi}{2}$.

EXAMPLE 5.4

Prove that the equation of the tangent to the hyperbola at $P(a\sec\theta, b\tan\theta)$ may be written as $\dfrac{x\sec\theta}{a} - \dfrac{y\tan\theta}{b} = 1$ or as $\dfrac{x}{a} - \dfrac{y}{b}\sin\theta = \cos\theta$.

SOLUTION

$x = a\sec\theta \Rightarrow \dfrac{dx}{d\theta} = a\sec\theta\tan\theta$ and $y = b\tan\theta \Rightarrow \dfrac{dy}{d\theta} = b\sec^2\theta$.

Therefore $\dfrac{dy}{dx} = \dfrac{b\sec^2\theta}{a\sec\theta\tan\theta} = \dfrac{b\sec\theta}{a\tan\theta}$ and the equation of the tangent at P is

$$y - b\tan\theta = \frac{b\sec\theta}{a\tan\theta}(x - a\sec\theta)$$

$$\Leftrightarrow \quad ay\tan\theta - ab\tan^2\theta = bx\sec\theta - ab\sec^2\theta$$

$$\Leftrightarrow \quad bx\sec\theta - ay\tan\theta = ab(\sec^2\theta - \tan^2\theta)$$

$$\Leftrightarrow \quad \frac{x\sec\theta}{a} - \frac{y\tan\theta}{b} = 1, \text{ since } \sec^2\theta - \tan^2\theta = 1.$$

Multiplying throughout by $\cos\theta$ and using $\tan\theta = \dfrac{\sin\theta}{\cos\theta}$ gives the alternative form $\dfrac{x}{a} - \dfrac{y}{b}\sin\theta = \cos\theta$.

You have already seen in the first activity of this section that the point $P(a\sec\theta, b\tan\theta)$ moves to infinity as $\theta \to \frac{\pi}{2}$. The second form of the equation of the tangent given in Example 5.4 shows that as this happens the tangent at P approaches the *asymptote* $\frac{x}{a} - \frac{y}{b} = 0$. Similarly the other asymptote $\frac{x}{a} + \frac{y}{b} = 0$ is the limiting position of the tangent as $\theta \to \frac{3\pi}{2}$.

ACTIVITY

Show that the family of hyperbolas $\frac{x^2}{a^2} - \frac{y^2}{b^2} = k$, where a and b are fixed but k varies, all have the same asymptotes. Sketch the curves for the values $k = 2, 1, \frac{1}{2}, 0, -\frac{1}{2}, -1, -2$.

ACTIVITY

Prove that the acute angle between an asymptote and the transverse axis is arcsec e.

Because their equations are so similar, the ellipse and the hyperbola share many properties. The obvious main differences between them are that the hyperbola has two branches and two asymptotes, so the distinctive features of the hyperbola usually involve the asymptotes.

EXAMPLE 5.5

Lines are drawn parallel to the asymptotes through any point P of the hyperbola $\frac{x^2}{a^2} - \frac{y^2}{b^2} = 1$, meeting the asymptotes at H and K. Prove that $PH \times PK = \frac{1}{4}(a^2 + b^2)$. (This property will be useful in the next section.)

SOLUTION

By symmetry there is no loss of generality in taking P to be $(a\sec\theta, b\tan\theta)$ in the first quadrant as in figure 5.14. Let $PH = h$, $PK = k$, and let the angle between the asymptote and the x axis be ϕ.

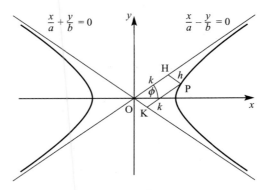

Figure 5.14

Then $\quad a\sec\theta = k\cos\phi + h\cos\phi \Rightarrow k + h = a\sec\theta\sec\phi$

and $\quad b\tan\theta = k\sin\phi - h\sin\phi \Rightarrow k - h = b\tan\theta\,\mathrm{cosec}\,\phi.$

So $\quad 4hk = (k+h)^2 - (k-h)^2$

$\quad\quad = a^2\sec^2\theta\sec^2\phi - b^2\tan^2\theta\,\mathrm{cosec}^2\phi$

$\quad\quad = (a\sec\phi)^2\sec^2\theta - (b\,\mathrm{cosec}\,\phi)^2\tan^2\theta.$

But since $\tan\phi = \dfrac{b}{a}$, $a\sec\phi = b\csc\phi = \sqrt{a^2 + b^2}$
(see figure 5.15).

Therefore $\qquad 4hk = (a^2 + b^2)(\sec^2\theta - \tan^2\theta) = (a^2 + b^2)$

and so $\qquad PH \times PK = \tfrac{1}{4}(a^2 + b^2)$.

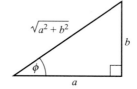

Figure 5.15

Throughout this exercise H is the hyperbola $\dfrac{x^2}{a^2} - \dfrac{y^2}{b^2} = 1$.

1 The rectangle TUVW has vertices (a, b), $(-a, b)$, $(-a, -b)$, $(a, -b)$ respectively. Show that

   (i) H touches TW and UV at their mid-points A and A$'$
   (ii) TV and UW are the asymptotes of H
   (iii) the circle with TV as diameter meets the x axis at the foci of H
   (iv) the directrices pass through the points where the circle with diameter AA$'$ meets the asymptotes.

2 Starting with the rectangle TUVW of Question 1 and using its properties, draw quick sketches of the following hyperbolas with their asymptotes, foci and directrices.

   (i) $\dfrac{x^2}{16} - \dfrac{y^2}{9} = 1$ $\qquad\qquad$ **(ii)** $\dfrac{x^2}{9} - \dfrac{y^2}{16} = 1$

   (iii) $\dfrac{x^2}{4} - y^2 = 1$ $\qquad\qquad$ **(iv)** $x^2 - y^2 = 36$

3 Find the equation of the hyperbola with foci $(\pm 8, 0)$ and directrices $x = \pm 2$.

4 Find the equation of the hyperbola which has asymptotes $y = \pm 3x$ and passes through $(2, 4)$. Find also the equations of the tangent and normal at $(2, 4)$.

5 Find the equations of the tangent and normal to the hyperbola $3x^2 - 2y^2 = 3$ at the point $(-5, 6)$. Find the x co-ordinate of the point where this normal meets the curve again.

6 The line $y = mx + c$ meets H at P_1, P_2 and meets the asymptotes at Q_1, Q_2.

   (i) Write down the quadratic equation whose roots are the x co-ordinates of P_1, P_2, and find the sum of these roots.
   (ii) Write down the quadratic equation whose roots are the x co-ordinates of Q_1, Q_2, and find the sum of these roots.
   (iii) Hence show that P_1, P_2 and Q_1, Q_2 have the same mid-point.
   (iv) Deduce that $P_1Q_1 = P_2Q_2$.

7 The tangent at a point P of H meets the asymptotes at Q_1, Q_2.

   (i) Prove that P is the mid-point of Q_1, Q_2. [**Hint:** Use Question 6 part **(iv)**.]
   (ii) Prove that as P varies the area of triangle OQ_1Q_2 remains constant.

8 The hyperbolas **H** and $\dfrac{x^2}{a^2} - \dfrac{y^2}{b^2} = -1$ are said to be *conjugate*.

Sketch both these hyperbolas on a single diagram.

If their eccentricities are e and f, show that $e^2 f^2 = e^2 + f^2$.

9 Prove that:

the line $y = mx + c$ touches $\mathbf{H} \Rightarrow a^2 m^2 = b^2 + c^2$.

Investigate whether the converse is true.

10 Prove that the equation of the normal to **H** at $P(a\sec\theta, b\tan\theta)$ is

$ax\sin\theta + by = (a^2 + b^2)\tan\theta$.

This normal meets the transverse axis at G, and the mid-point of PG is Q. Prove that the locus of Q is a hyperbola.

11 (i) Show that the x co-ordinates of the points of intersection of the line

$y = mx + c$ and the hyperbola $\dfrac{x^2}{a^2} - \dfrac{y^2}{b^2} = 1$ satisfy the quadratic equation

$$(a^2 m^2 - b^2)x^2 + (2a^2 mc)x + a^2(c^2 + b^2) = 0.$$

(ii) Deduce that if $y = mx + c$ is a tangent to the hyperbola, then $c^2 = a^2 m^2 - b^2$.

(iii) A tangent to the hyperbola has gradient m and passes through the point R with co-ordinates (p, q). Show that

$$(a^2 - p^2)m^2 + 2pqm - (b^2 + q^2) = 0.$$

Two tangents to the hyperbola, with gradients m_1 and m_2, intersect at the point R.

(iv) Express $m_1 + m_2$ and $m_1 m_2$ in terms of a, b, p and q.

(v) If the two tangents are perpendicular, show that R lies on the circle with centre the origin and radius $\sqrt{a^2 - b^2}$ (provided that $a > b$).

12 (i) Prove that the lines $\dfrac{x}{a} + \dfrac{y}{b} = t$, $\dfrac{x}{a} - \dfrac{y}{b} = \dfrac{1}{t}$ $(t \neq 0)$, which are parallel to the asymptotes, meet on **H**.

(ii) Deduce the alternative parametric equations $x = \dfrac{a}{2}\left(t + \dfrac{1}{t}\right)$, $y = \dfrac{b}{2}\left(t - \dfrac{1}{t}\right)$ for **H**.

(iii) The same point of **H** has co-ordinates $(a\sec\theta, b\tan\theta)$ and $\left(\dfrac{a}{2}\left(t + \dfrac{1}{t}\right), \dfrac{b}{2}\left(t - \dfrac{1}{t}\right)\right)$.

Prove that $t = \tan\left(\dfrac{\theta}{2} + \dfrac{\pi}{4}\right)$.

(iv) Show that the equation of the tangent to **H** at $\left(\dfrac{a}{2}\left(t + \dfrac{1}{t}\right), \dfrac{b}{2}\left(t - \dfrac{1}{t}\right)\right)$ is

$$\dfrac{x}{a}(t^2 + 1) - \dfrac{y}{b}(t^2 - 1) = 2t.$$

(v) Find where the tangent in part **(iv)** meets the asymptotes, and deduce the results of Question 7 again.

The rectangular hyperbola

In the special case when $a = b$ the equation of the hyperbola may be written as $x^2 - y^2 = a^2$, and the asymptotes are the lines $y = \pm x$. Since these are at right angles the curve is called a *rectangular hyperbola* (see figure 5.16).

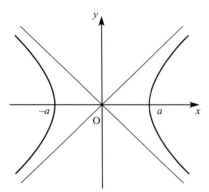

Figure 5.16

ACTIVITY

Show that all rectangular hyperbolas have eccentricity $\sqrt{2}$, and hence that they are all the same shape. (The relationship between rectangular hyperbolas and general hyperbolas is like that between circles and ellipses.)

Since the asymptotes of a rectangular hyperbola are perpendicular they can be used as co-ordinate axes. Let $P(x, y)$ be a point on a rectangular hyperbola referred to these axes, with one branch in the first quadrant (see figure 5.17).

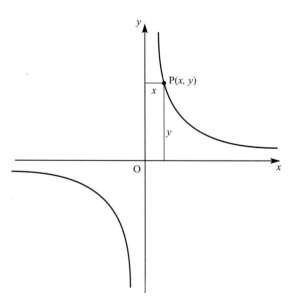

Figure 5.17

The lines through P parallel to the asymptotes have lengths x and y in this case, so the result of Example 5.5 becomes $xy = \frac{1}{4}(a^2 + a^2) = \frac{1}{2}a^2$. Putting $c^2 = \frac{1}{2}a^2$ gives the equation of a rectangular hyperbola referred to its asymptotes as co-ordinate axes in the very simple form $xy = c^2$. The particular case $c = 1$ shows that the familiar curve of reciprocals $y = \frac{1}{x}$ is a rectangular hyperbola.

The curve $xy = c^2$ has the simple parametric equations $x = ct$, $y = \frac{c}{t}$, where $t \neq 0$.

ACTIVITY

Check that the point $\left(ct, \frac{c}{t}\right)$ lies on $xy = c^2$ and that every point of the curve corresponds to one and only one non-zero value of t. Describe how $\left(ct, \frac{c}{t}\right)$ moves along the curve as t increases from $-\infty$ to ∞.

The gradient of the chord joining the points $\left(ct, \frac{c}{t}\right)$ and $\left(cu, \frac{c}{u}\right)$ is

$$\frac{\frac{c}{u} - \frac{c}{t}}{cu - ct} = \frac{\left(\frac{t-u}{tu}\right)}{u - t} = -\frac{1}{tu}.$$

Therefore the equation of the chord is $y - \frac{c}{t} = -\frac{1}{tu}(x - ct)$

$$\Leftrightarrow \quad tuy - cu = -x + ct$$
$$\Leftrightarrow \quad x + tuy = c(t + u).$$

By letting $u \to t$ you can see that the equation of the tangent to $xy = c^2$ at the point $\left(ct, \frac{c}{t}\right)$ is $x + t^2 y = 2ct$.

EXAMPLE 5.6

The vertices of a triangle are on a rectangular hyperbola. Prove that the orthocentre of the triangle is also on this hyperbola.

(The *orthocentre* of a triangle is the point where the three perpendiculars from the vertices to the opposite edges meet.)

SOLUTION

Let the triangle be $P_1P_2P_3$, and let the perpendicular from P_3 to P_1P_2 meet the hyperbola again at P_4 (see figure 5.18).

Let the parameter of each P_i be t_i ($i = 1, 2, 3, 4$). The gradient of P_1P_2 is $-\frac{1}{t_1 t_2}$ and the gradient of P_3P_4 is $-\frac{1}{t_3 t_4}$. Since these lines are perpendicular the product of their gradients is -1. Therefore $t_1 t_2 t_3 t_4 = -1$. But this condition is symmetrical in t_1, t_2, t_3, t_4 and so P_1P_4 is also perpendicular to P_2P_3. Therefore P_4 also lies on the perpendicular from P_1 to P_2P_3, and so P_4 is the orthocentre of triangle $P_1P_2P_3$.

Similarly each of P_1, P_2, P_3 is the orthocentre of the triangle formed by the other three points.

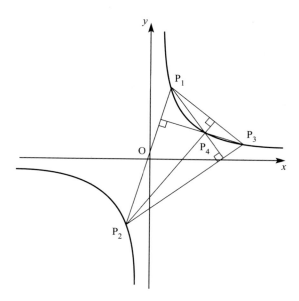

Figure 5.18

Before doing Exercise 5D remind yourself of the properties of roots of polynomial equations (summarised on page 23), which you may find useful.

(summarised on page 23)

EXERCISE 5D

Throughout this exercise R is the rectangular hyperbola $xy = c^2$.

1 The tangent at a point P of R meets the co-ordinate axes at U and V. Prove that UV and OP make equal angles with the co-ordinate axes. Deduce that P is the mid-point of UV.

2 Find the co-ordinates of the foci and the equations of the directrices of R.

3 Find the co-ordinates of the two points where the hyperbolas $x^2 - y^2 = 5$ and $xy = 6$ intersect. Prove that the tangents to the hyperbolas at these points form a rectangle.

4 The tangents at the points P and Q of R meet at T. Prove that the line joining T to the mid-point of PQ passes through the origin.

5 Sketch on a single diagram three members of each of the following families of rectangular hyperbolas:

(A) those with equations $x^2 - y^2 = a^2$ for various a
(B) those with equations $xy = c^2$ for various c.

Prove that every member of family (A) meets every member of family (B) at right angles, unless $a = c = 0$.

6 The parametric equations of a rectangular hyperbola are $x = ct$, $y = \dfrac{c}{t}$, where c is a constant.

  (i) A straight line $y = ax + b$ meets the hyperbola at two points P and Q, with parameters t_1 and t_2 respectively.

    (a) Find a quadratic equation (with coefficients in terms of a, b and c) whose roots are t_1 and t_2.

    Deduce that $t_1 t_2 = -\dfrac{1}{a}$, and find an expression for $t_1 + t_2$.

    (b) The line PQ crosses the x axis at A and the y axis at B. Write down the x co-ordinates of P, A, B and Q, and hence show that PA = BQ.

  (ii) **(a)** Find the equation of the normal to the hyperbola at $R\left(cr, \dfrac{c}{r}\right)$.

    (b) The normal at R meets the hyperbola again at the point S with parameter s. Using the results in **(i) (a)** and **(ii) (a)**, or otherwise, show that $s = -\dfrac{1}{r^3}$.

                                                [MEI]

7 Find the equation of the normal to $\boldsymbol{R}$ at the point $P\left(ct, \dfrac{c}{t}\right)$. Prove that this normal meets the hyperbola again at $Q\left(-\dfrac{c}{t^3}, -ct^3\right)$.

The circle with PQ as diameter meets $\boldsymbol{R}$ again at N. Prove that PN passes through the origin, and that the normal at N is parallel to PQ.

8 The mid-point of the chord joining $\left(ct, \dfrac{c}{t}\right)$ and $\left(cT, \dfrac{c}{T}\right)$ has co-ordinates (X, Y).

Prove that $t + T = \dfrac{2X}{c}$ and $tT = \dfrac{X}{Y}$.

A variable chord of $\boldsymbol{R}$ passes through the fixed point (h, k). Prove that the locus of the mid-point of the chord is another rectangular hyperbola, and give the equations of its asymptotes.

9 In this question P, Q, R, S are points on $\boldsymbol{R}$ with parameters p, q, r, s respectively.

  (i) Form a fourth degree equation in t by substituting $x = ct$, $y = \dfrac{c}{t}$ in

$$x^2 + y^2 + 2gx + 2fy + k = 0.$$

  Deduce that if P, Q, R, S are concyclic (i.e. lie on a circle) then $pqrs = 1$.

  (ii) Prove the converse of the result in **(i)**, i.e. $pqrs = 1 \Rightarrow$ P, Q, R, S are concyclic.

  (iii) Prove that if P, Q, R, S lie on a circle and PQ is a diameter of $\boldsymbol{R}$ then RS is a diameter of the circle.

  (iv) A variable circle touches $\boldsymbol{R}$ at a fixed point P and meets $\boldsymbol{R}$ again at variable points R and S. Prove that the chord RS has a fixed direction.

  (v) The normal to $\boldsymbol{R}$ at P meets the hyperbola again at P′, and Q′, R′, S′ are defined similarly. Prove that:

    P, Q, R, S are concyclic $\Leftrightarrow$ P′, Q′, R′, S′ are concyclic.

	Ellipse	Parabola	Hyperbola	Rectangular hyperbola
Standard form	$\dfrac{x^2}{a^2} + \dfrac{y^2}{b^2} = 1$	$y^2 = 4ax$	$\dfrac{x^2}{a^2} - \dfrac{y^2}{b^2} = 1$	$xy = c^2$
Parametric form	$(a\cos\theta,\, b\sin\theta)$	$(at^2,\, 2at)$	$(a\sec\theta,\, b\tan\theta)$	$\left(ct,\, \dfrac{c}{t}\right)$
Eccentricity	$e < 1$ $b^2 = a^2(1 - e^2)$	$e = 1$	$e > 1$ $b^2 = a^2(e^2 - 1)$	$e = \sqrt{2}$
Foci	$(\pm ae,\, 0)$	$(a,\, 0)$	$(\pm ae,\, 0)$	$(\sqrt{2}c,\, \sqrt{2}c),$ $(-\sqrt{2}c,\, -\sqrt{2}c)$
Directrices	$x = \pm\dfrac{a}{e}$	$x = -a$	$x = \pm\dfrac{a}{e}$	$x + y = \pm\sqrt{2}c$
Asymptotes	none	none	$\dfrac{x}{a} = \pm\dfrac{y}{b}$	$x = 0,\, y = 0$

6 Power series

This discovery has been forced on us by the realisation that we are approaching the limits of something.

Gary Snyder, 1930

Polynomial approximations

Since polynomial functions are easy to evaluate, to differentiate or to integrate they can be useful as approximations to more complicated functions. Here is one way of finding such approximations, using the exponential function as an example.

If you want to use a straight line to approximate the curve with equation $y = e^x$, there are many straight lines you could choose. Even restricting your choice to those which are tangents, there are infinitely many lines you could choose. The most obvious straight line to use is the tangent to the curve at the point where $x = 0$, as illustrated in figure 6.1. Suppose the tangent has equation $y = a_0 + a_1 x$; then:

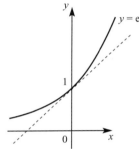

Figure 6.1

① line and curve cut the y axis at the same point $\Rightarrow a_0 = e^0 = 1$;

② line and curve have the same gradient when $x = 0 \Rightarrow a_1 = 1$ since $\dfrac{d}{dx}(e^x) = e^x$, which is 1 when $x = 0$.

So the linear approximation for e^x is $1 + x$.

But straight lines are straight, and are not really suitable for approximating to curves over any distance. Using the quadratic equation,

$$y = a_0 + a_1 x + a_2 x^2$$

to approximate to $y = e^x$, as shown in figure 6.2, requires as before, that:

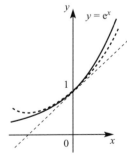

Figure 6.2

① both curves cut the y axis at the same point $\Rightarrow a_0 = e^0 = 1$;

② both curves have the same gradient when $x = 0 \Rightarrow a_1 = e^0 = 1$;

but now: ③ both curves must have the same second derivative when $x = 0$.

Since $\dfrac{d^2}{dx^2}(e^x) = e^x$, which is 1 when $x = 0$, and $\dfrac{d^2}{dx^2}(a_0 + a_1 x + a_2 x^2) = 2a_2$,

③ $\Rightarrow 2a_2 = 1 \Rightarrow a_2 = \frac{1}{2}$. So the quadratic approximation for e^x is $1 + x + \frac{1}{2}x^2$.

Extending this to finding the cubic $a_0 + a_1 x + a_2 x^2 + a_3 x^3$ that approximates to e^x brings in the additional requirement that the cubic and e^x have the same third derivative at $x = 0$. Now $\dfrac{d^3}{dx^3}(a_0 + a_1 x + a_2 x^2 + a_3 x^3) = 3 \times 2a_3 = 3!a_3$ and $\dfrac{d^3}{dx^3}(e^x) = e^x = 1$ when $x = 0$ so you require $a_3 = \dfrac{1}{3!}$. The cubic approximation for e^x is $1 + x + \dfrac{1}{2!}x^2 + \dfrac{1}{3!}x^3$.

Figure 6.3 shows the graph of $y = e^x$ together with the graphs of the linear, quadratic and cubic approximations you have just constructed. The graph shows that, for positive x, the accuracy of the approximation improves as more terms are used. Using more terms also improves the accuracy when x is negative, though the diagram alone does not justify that claim.

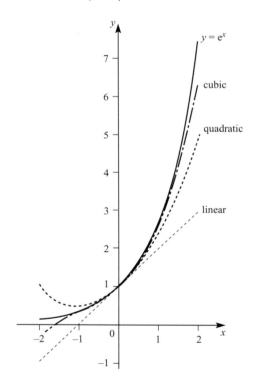

Figure 6.3

ACTIVITY

The cubic approximation for e^x is $1 + x + \dfrac{x^2}{2} + \dfrac{x^3}{6}$. Write down a cubic approximation for e^{-x}. Multiply the two approximations together and comment on your answer.

ACTIVITY

Show that the next (i.e. the fourth degree) approximation for e^x is $1 + x + \dfrac{x^2}{2!} + \dfrac{x^3}{3!} + \dfrac{x^4}{4!}$. Hence show that $e \approx 1 + 1 + \dfrac{1}{2!} + \dfrac{1}{3!} + \dfrac{1}{4!}$ and evaluate this approximation correct to 3 decimal places.

This is typical of the general case. Suppose $f(x)$ is a function, that its first n derivatives exist at $x = 0$, and that you want to find a polynomial $p(x)$ of degree n which has the same values as $f(x)$ and its first n derivatives at $x = 0$. Then

$$p(0) = f(0), \, p'(0) = f'(0), \, p''(0) = f''(0), \, \ldots, \, p^{(n)}(0) = f^{(n)}(0).$$

Note the symbol for the nth derivative of $p(x)$, evaluated at $x = 0$.

Solving these $n + 1$ equations gives the $n + 1$ coefficients needed for a polynomial of degree n.

If $p(x) \equiv a_0 + a_1 x + a_2 x^2 + a_3 x^3 + \cdots + a_r x^r + \cdots + a_n x^n$ then $p(0) = a_0 = f(0)$ and

$p'(x) \equiv a_1 + 2a_2 x + 3a_3 x^2 + \cdots + r a_r x^{r-1} + \cdots + n a_n x^{n-1}$ $\Rightarrow p'(0) = a_1 = f'(0)$;

$p''(x) \equiv 2a_2 + 6a_3 x + \cdots + r(r-1)a_r x^{r-2} + \cdots + n(n-1)a_n x^{n-2}$ $\Rightarrow p''(0) = 2a_2 = f''(0)$;

$p^{(3)}(x) \equiv 6a_3 + \cdots + r(r-1)(r-2)a_r x^{r-3} + \cdots + n(n-1)(n-2)a_n x^{n-3} \Rightarrow p^{(3)}(0) = 6a_3 = f^{(3)}(0)$;

and so on. Generalising:

$p^{(r)}(x) \equiv r! a_r + \cdots + n(n-1)(n-2) \cdots (n-r+1)a_n x^{n-r}$ $\Rightarrow p^{(r)}(0) = r! a_r = f^{(r)}(0)$;

and $p^{(n)}(x) \equiv n! a_n$ $\Rightarrow p^{(n)}(0) = n! a_n = f^{(n)}(0)$.

The last equality on each line gives

$$a_0 = f(0), \, a_1 = f'(0), \, a_2 = \tfrac{1}{2}f''(0), \, a_3 = \tfrac{1}{6}f^{(3)}(0), \, \cdots, \, a_r = \frac{1}{r!}f^{(r)}(0), \, \cdots, \, a_n = \frac{1}{n!}f^{(n)}(0).$$

Putting all these together produces the approximation

$$f(x) \approx f(0) + x f'(0) + \frac{x^2}{2!}f''(0) + \frac{x^3}{3!}f^{(3)}(0) + \cdots + \frac{x^r}{r!}f^{(r)}(0) + \cdots + \frac{x^n}{n!}f^{(n)}(0).$$

This is known as the *Maclaurin expansion* for $f(x)$ as far as the term in x^n, or the nth *Maclaurin approximation* for $f(x)$.

EXAMPLE 6.1   Find the Maclaurin expansion for $(1 - x)^{-1}$ as far as x^n.

SOLUTION

Let $f(x) \equiv (1 - x)^{-1}$.

$f(x) \equiv (1 - x)^{-1}$	$f(0) = 1$
$f'(x) \equiv (1 - x)^{-2}$	$f'(0) = 1$
$f''(x) \equiv 2(1 - x)^{-3}$	$f''(0) = 2$
$f^{(3)}(x) \equiv 6(1 - x)^{-4}$	$f^{(3)}(0) = 6$
$f^{(4)}(x) \equiv 24(1 - x)^{-5}$	$f^{(4)}(0) = 24$
$\vdots$	$\vdots$
$f^{(n)}(x) \equiv n!(1 - x)^{-(n+1)}$	$f^{(n)}(0) = n!$

Tabulate $f(x)$ and its derivatives and evaluate them at $x = 0$.

Then $(1 - x)^{-1} \approx 1 + x + x^2 + x^3 + x^4 + \cdots + x^n$.

EXERCISE 6A

1 Find the Maclaurin expansion up to the term in x^4 for each of these functions.

(i) $\sin x$ (ii) $\cos x$
(iii) $\tan x$ (iv) $\sinh x$
(v) $\cosh x$ (vi) $\tanh x$

2 This flow diagram gives a method for calculating e. Explain why. Carry out this calculation, working to 8 decimal places, and show that e = 2.718282 (to 6 decimal places).

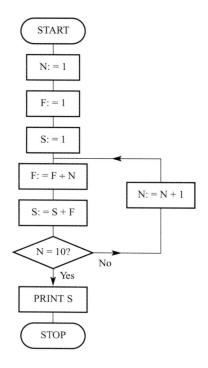

3 Use a Maclaurin approximation to calculate $\dfrac{1}{\sqrt{e}}$ to 5 decimal places.

4 Use the cubic approximation to $\sin x$ to show that the positive root of $\sin x = x^2$ is approximately $\sqrt{15} - 3$.

5 The third Maclaurin approximation to $f(x)$ is $1 - \frac{3}{2}x^2 + \frac{5}{2}x^3$. Write down the values of $f'(0)$, $f''(0)$, $f^{(3)}(0)$. Sketch the graph of $y = f(x)$ near $x = 0$.

6 If $E_n(x) = \displaystyle\sum_{r=0}^{n} \frac{x^r}{r!}$ show that

(i) $E_n'(x) = E_{n-1}(x)$

(ii) $\displaystyle\int E_n(x)\,dx = E_{n+1}(x) + c.$

Explain how these results are linked to properties of e^x.

7 An approximate rule used by builders to find the length, c, of a circular arc ABC is

$$c = \frac{8b - a}{3},$$

where a and b are as shown in the diagram.

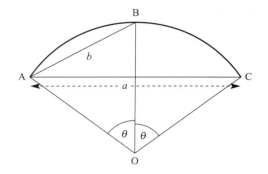

(i) If O is the centre of the circle, show that $b = 2r\sin\frac{\theta}{2}$ and $a = 2r\sin\theta$.

(ii) Using the cubic approximation to $\sin x$, show that $8b - a = 6r\theta$. Hence verify the rule.

(iii) Find the percentage error caused by using this rule when $\theta = \frac{\pi}{3}$.

8 A surveyor measures a length AB on sloping ground. Before he plots A and B on the map he must find the horizontal distance AC between them.

An approximate rule used by surveyors for reducing a sloping length of 100 metres to its horizontal equivalent is 'Square the number of degrees in the slope, multiply by $1\frac{1}{2}$ and obtain the *correction* in centimetres.'

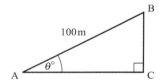

If the slope $\theta°$ equals α radians, show that the correction is about $5000\alpha^2$ centimetres. Show that the rule is approximately correct for gentle slopes.

9 Write down the Maclaurin series for $e^{-\frac{1}{2}x^2}$

(i) as far as x^6

(ii) as far as x^8.

It can be shown that $e^{-\frac{1}{2}x^2}$ always lies between these two approximations. Use them to estimate $\int_0^1 e^{-\frac{1}{2}x^2}\,dx$ and to establish error bounds for your answer. (It is not possible to find $\int e^{-\frac{1}{2}x^2}\,dx$ explicitly, but finding good approximations for integrals such as $\int_a^b e^{-\frac{1}{2}x^2}\,dx$ was an essential part of the construction of the normal distribution tables, a key tool in statistics.)

10 (i) Prove by induction that

$$f(x) \equiv e^x \sin x \Rightarrow f^{(n)}(x) \equiv 2^{n/2}e^x\sin\left(x + \frac{n\pi}{4}\right)$$

and use this result to obtain the Maclaurin series for $e^x \sin x$ as far as x^6.

(ii) Multiply the third Maclaurin approximation for e^x by the third Maclaurin approximation for $\sin x$, and comment on your result.

(iii) Find a Maclaurin approximation for $e^x \cos x$ by multiplying the third Maclaurin approximation for e^x by the fourth Maclaurin approximation for $\cos x$, giving as many terms in your answer as you think justifiable.

Maclaurin series

At this stage it is not possible to say much about the accuracy of these Maclaurin approximations. But the nth Maclaurin expansion for $(1 - x)^{-1}$, obtained in Example 6.1, is the geometric progression $1 + x + x^2 + x^3 + x^4 + \cdots + x^n$; if you let n tend to infinity you obtain the infinite geometric series

$1 + x + x^2 + x^3 + x^4 + \cdots$ which, if $|x| < 1$, converges to $\dfrac{1}{1 - x} \equiv (1 - x)^{-1}$, known as its *sum to infinity*.

This means that, provided $|x| < 1$, by taking sufficiently many terms you can make the Maclaurin expansion of $(1 - x)^{-1}$ as close to $(1 - x)^{-1}$ as you like. But the geometric series $1 + x + x^2 + x^3 + x^4 + \cdots$ does not converge if $|x| \geqslant 1$.

Generalising these ideas: if the function $f(x)$ and all its derivatives exist at $x = 0$, then the infinite series

$$f(0) + xf'(0) + \frac{x^2}{2!}f''(0) + \frac{x^3}{3!}f^{(3)}(0) + \cdots + \frac{x^r}{r!}f^{(r)}(0) + \cdots$$

is known as the *Maclaurin series* for $f(x)$. If the sum of this series up to and including the term in x^n (i.e. the sum of the first $n + 1$ terms) tends to a limit as n tends to infinity, and this limit is $f(x)$, you say that the expansion *converges* to $f(x)$. For some functions, for example $(1 - x)^{-1}$, the series only converges for a limited range of values of x; these are described as the values for which the series is *valid*. A more detailed examination of the validity of the Maclaurin series will be given in Chapter 2 of *Pure Mathematics 6*, but for now the values of x for which the common Maclaurin series are valid are merely stated, without proof.

This chapter started by developing Maclaurin expansions for e^x. Since e^x and all its derivatives are identical, and $e^x = 1$ when $x = 0$, the Maclaurin series for e^x is

$$1 + x + \frac{x^2}{2!} + \frac{x^3}{3!} + \cdots + \frac{x^r}{r!} + \cdots .$$

This series is valid for all x.

EXAMPLE 6.2

Find the Maclaurin series for $\sin x$.

SOLUTION

Let $f(x) \equiv \sin x$.

$f(x) \equiv \sin x$	$f(0) = 0$
$f'(x) \equiv \cos x$	$f'(0) = 1$
$f''(x) \equiv -\sin x$	$f''(0) = 0$
$f^{(3)}(x) \equiv -\cos x$	$f^{(3)}(0) = -1$
$f^{(4)}(x) \equiv \sin x$	$f^{(4)}(0) = 0$

Tabulate $f(x)$ and its derivatives and evaluate them at $x = 0$.

$$f^{(2r+1)}(x) \equiv (-1)^r \cos x \qquad f^{(2r+1)}(0) = (-1)^r$$

$$f^{(2r+2)}(x) \equiv (-1)^{r+1} \sin x \qquad f^{(2r+2)}(0) = 0$$

$$f^{(2r+3)}(x) \equiv (-1)^{r+1} \cos x \qquad f^{(2r+3)}(0) = (-1)^{r+1}$$

$$f^{(2r+4)}(x) \equiv (-1)^{r+2} \sin x \qquad f^{(2r+4)}(0) = 0$$

Then $\sin x = x - \dfrac{x^3}{3!} + \dfrac{x^5}{5!} - \dfrac{x^7}{7!} + \cdots + \dfrac{(-1)^r x^{2r+1}}{(2r+1)!} + \cdots$.

Note the connection between these terms and the fact that $\sin x$ is an odd function.

(This series is valid for all values of x.)

ACTIVITY

Show that the Maclaurin series for $\cos x$ is $1 - \dfrac{x^2}{2!} + \dfrac{x^4}{4!} - \dfrac{x^6}{6!} + \cdots + \dfrac{(-1)^r x^{2r}}{(2r)!} + \cdots$.

(This series is also valid for all x. Notice that the first two terms here form the familiar approximation for $\cos x$ when x is small, and that, as you might expect, the series for $\cos x$ is the same as the series obtained by differentiating the $\sin x$ series term by term.)

ACTIVITY

Show that the Maclaurin series for $(1 + x)^n$ is

$$1 + nx + \frac{n(n-1)}{2!} x^2 + \cdots + \frac{n(n-1)\ldots(n-r+1)}{r!} x^r + \cdots$$

i.e. the familiar binomial series for $(1 + x)^n$.

If n is a positive integer: the series terminates after $n + 1$ terms, and is valid for all x.

If n is not a positive integer: the series is valid for $|x| < 1$, but not valid for $|x| > 1$; the series is also valid for $x = 1$ if $n > -1$, and for $x = -1$ if $n > 0$.

Figure 6.4 shows the graph of the function $(1 + x)^{-\frac{1}{2}}$ and several successive Maclaurin approximations. It illustrates the fact that the approximations converge on $(1 + x)^{-\frac{1}{2}}$ if $|x| < 1$, but not if $x > 1$. At first sight the graph may appear to show that successive approximations also converge when $x < -1$; but they cannot be converging on $(1 + x)^{-\frac{1}{2}}$, which is undefined for $x \leqslant -1$.

ACTIVITY

(i) Explain why it is not possible to find Maclaurin expansions for $\ln x$.

(ii) (a) Show that the Maclaurin series for $\ln(1 + x)$ is

$$x - \frac{x^2}{2} + \frac{x^3}{3} - \cdots + \frac{(-1)^{n+1} x^n}{n} + \cdots.$$

(b) This series is valid for $-1 < x \leqslant 1$ only; by drawing graphs of $y = \ln(1 + x)$ and several successive approximations show that this is plausible.

(This series was first found by Nicolaus Mercator (1620–87), who lived for many years in London, though he was born in Denmark.)

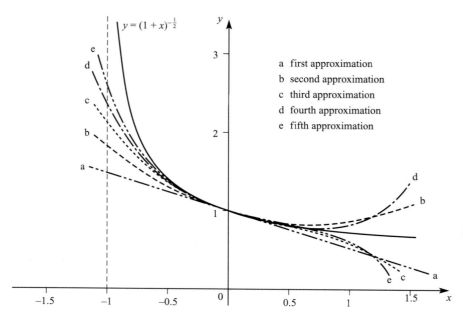

Figure 6.4

1 Find the Maclaurin series for $\cosh x$, including the general term,

    (i)   by finding the values of successive derivatives at $x = 0$

    (ii) by using the definition $\cosh x = \frac{1}{2}(e^x + e^{-x})$.

(The Maclaurin series for $\cosh x$ and $\sinh x$ are valid for all values of x.)

2 (i) **(a)** Show, by successive differentiation of $\sinh x$, that its Maclaurin series is

$$x + \frac{x^3}{3!} + \frac{x^5}{5!} + \cdots.$$

    (b) Write down the series for $\sinh(x^2)$ in ascending powers of x, giving the first three non-zero terms and the general term.

    (c) Given that $f(x) = \sinh(x^2)$, use the series in part **(i)(b)** to find the values of $f^{(5)}(0)$ and $f^{(6)}(0)$. [$f^{(n)}(x)$ denotes the nth derivative of $f(x)$.]

    (ii) Use the series in part **(i)(b)** to find the value of

$$\int_0^{0.6} x^2 \sinh(x^2)\, dx$$

correct to 4 decimal places

[MEI, part]

3 A graphic calculator or graph-drawing software will be useful in this question.

    (i)   Draw a graph of $y = \sin x$. On the same axes draw graphs of the first few Maclaurin approximations to $\sin x$.

    (ii) Repeat **(i)** for **(a)** $\cos x$ **(b)** $(1 + x)^{-1}$ **(c)** $(1 + x)^{0.5}$.

4 Find the Maclaurin expansion of $f(x) = \dfrac{e^x}{e^x + 1}$ as far as the term in x^3.

Show that no even powers of x can occur in the full expansion.

[**Hint for the last part**: Show that $f(x) - f(0)$ is an odd function.]

5 In this question give all numerical answers to 4 decimal places.

(i) Put $x = 1$ in the expansion

$$\ln(1 + x) \approx x - \frac{x^2}{2} + \frac{x^3}{3} - \cdots - \frac{x^{10}}{10}$$

and calculate an estimate of $\ln 2$. (Approximately 1000 terms would be needed to obtain $\ln 2$ correct to 3 decimal places by this method.)

(ii) Show that $\ln 2 = -\ln(1 - \frac{1}{2})$ and hence estimate $\ln 2$ by summing six terms.

(iii) Write down the series for $\ln(1 + x) - \ln(1 - x)$ as far as the first three non-zero terms and estimate $\ln 2$ by summing these terms using a suitable value of x.

6 (i) By differentiating the equation $\tanh y = x$, show that $\dfrac{d}{dx}(\operatorname{artanh} x) = \dfrac{1}{1 - x^2}$.

(ii) Using integration by parts, find $\int \operatorname{artanh} x \, dx$.

(iii) Prove that $\operatorname{artanh} x = \frac{1}{2}\ln\left(\dfrac{1 + x}{1 - x}\right)$.

(iv) Show that $\int_0^{\frac{1}{2}} \operatorname{artanh} x \, dx = \frac{1}{4}\ln\left(\frac{27}{16}\right)$.

(v) Show that the expansion of $\operatorname{artanh} x$ in ascending powers of x begins $x + \frac{1}{3}x^3 + \cdots$.

[**MEI**]

7 A curve passes through the point $(0, 2)$; its gradient is given by the differential equation $\dfrac{dy}{dx} = 1 - xy$. Assume that the equation of this curve can be expressed as the Maclaurin series

$$y = a_0 + a_1 x + a_2 x^2 + a_3 x^3 + a_4 x^4 + \cdots .$$

(i) Find a_0 and show that

$$a_1 + 2a_2 x + 3a_3 x^2 + 4a_4 x^3 + \cdots = 1 - 2x - a_1 x^2 - a_2 x^3 - a_3 x^4 - \cdots .$$

(ii) Equate coefficients to find the first seven terms of the Maclaurin series.

(iii) Draw graphs to compare the solution given by these seven terms with a solution generated (step by step) on a computer.

8 (i) Write down the Maclaurin expansions of

(a) $\cos\theta$　　　　　**(b)** $\sin\theta$　　　　　**(c)** $\cos\theta + j\sin\theta$,

giving series **(c)** in ascending powers of θ.

(ii) Substitute $x = j\theta$ in the Maclaurin series for e^x and simplify the terms.

(iii) Show that the series in parts **(i)(c)** and **(ii)** are the same.

(This confirms that the definition $e^{j\theta} = \cos\theta + j\sin\theta$ given on page 43 is consistent with the Maclaurin series of the functions involved.)

9 In this question y_n and a_n are used to denote $f^{(n)}(x)$ and $f^{(n)}(0)$ respectively.

  (i) Let $f(x) = \arcsin x$. Show that $(1 - x^2)y_1^2 = 1$ and $(1 - x^2)y_2 - xy_1 = 0$.

  (ii) Find a_1 and a_2.

  (iii) Prove by induction that $(1 - x^2)y_{n+2} - (2n + 1)xy_{n+1} - n^2y_n = 0$, and deduce that $a_{n+2} = n^2 a_n$.

  (iv) Find the Maclaurin expansion of $\arcsin x$, giving the first three non-zero terms and the general term.

Alternative approaches

Sometimes finding the coefficients of a Maclaurin series by repeated differentiation can be very laborious. As shown in the next example, the problem can be eased if you can express a derivative in terms of earlier derivatives, or the original function.

EXAMPLE 6.3   Find the first four non-zero terms of the Maclaurin series for $e^{2x}\sin 3x$.

SOLUTION

Let $f(x) \equiv e^{2x}\sin 3x.$ $f(0) = 0.$

Then $f'(x) \equiv 2e^{2x}\sin 3x + 3e^{2x}\cos 3x$

              $\equiv 2f(x) + 3e^{2x}\cos 3x$ $f'(0) = 3$

and $f''(x) \equiv 2f'(x) + 6e^{2x}\cos 3x - 9e^{2x}\sin 3x$ *Expressing $f''(x)$ in terms of $f'(x)$ and $f(x)$ simplifies further differentiation.*

              $\equiv 2f'(x) + 2(f'(x) - 2f(x)) - 9f(x)$

              $\equiv 4f'(x) - 13f(x)$ $f''(0) = 12.$

Then $f^{(3)}(x) \equiv 4f''(x) - 13f'(x)$ $f^{(3)}(0) = 48 - 39 = 9$

and $f^{(4)}(x) \equiv 4f^{(3)}(x) - 13f''(x)$, etc. $f^{(4)}(0) = 36 - 156 = -120.$

Thus $e^{2x}\sin 3x = 3x + \dfrac{x^2}{2!} \times 12 + \dfrac{x^3}{3!} \times 9 - \dfrac{x^4}{4!} \times 120 + \cdots$

                    $= 3x + 6x^2 + \dfrac{3}{2}x^3 - 5x^4 + \cdots.$

Sometimes a Maclaurin series can be found by adapting one or more known Maclaurin series. Some such methods are indicated in the next activity. You may well wonder whether the processes used are justifiable. Is it legitimate (for example) to integrate (or differentiate) an infinite series term by term? Can you form the product of two infinite series by multiplying terms? Is the series obtained identical to the series that would have been obtained by evaluating the derivatives? Answering these important questions in detail is beyond the scope of this book, though generally the answer is 'Yes, subject to certain conditions'.

ACTIVITY

Try out the following methods and explain why they work. How would you obtain further terms of the required series?

(i) The Maclaurin series for $\ln(1 + x)$ can be found by integrating the terms of the binomial series for $(1 + x)^{-1}$. Why is the integration constant zero?

(ii) The start of the Maclaurin series for $\dfrac{e^x}{1 + x}$ can be found by multiplying together the first four terms of the Maclaurin series for e^x and $(1 + x)^{-1}$ and discarding all terms in x^4 and higher powers.

(iii) The first few terms of the Maclaurin series for $\sec x$ can be found from the first three terms of the Maclaurin series for $(1 + y)^{-1}$ where

$$y = -\frac{x^2}{2!} + \frac{x^4}{4!}.$$

Taylor approximations

All Maclaurin expansions are 'centred' on $x = 0$. But it is possible to form expansions centred elsewhere:

let $g(h) \equiv f(a + h)$ where a is the constant $x - h$;

then $g'(h) \equiv f'(a + h)$, $g''(h) \equiv f''(a + h)$, etc.,

and $g(0) = f(a)$, $g'(0) = f'(a)$, $g''(0) = f''(a)$, etc. so that

$$f(a + h) \equiv g(h) \approx g(0) + hg'(0) + \frac{h^2}{2!}g''(0) + \frac{h^3}{3!}g^{(3)}(0) + \cdots + \frac{h^n}{n!}g^{(n)}(0).$$

This may be expressed in either of the following two ways:

$$f(a + h) \approx f(a) + hf'(a) + \frac{h^2}{2!}f''(a) + \frac{h^3}{3!}f^{(3)}(a) + \cdots + \frac{h^n}{n!}f^{(n)}(a).$$

or equivalently

$$f(x) \approx f(a) + (x - a)f'(a) + \frac{(x - a)^2}{2!}f''(a) + \frac{(x - a)^3}{3!}f^{(3)}(a) + \cdots + \frac{(x - a)^n}{n!}f^{(n)}(a).$$

These two formulae are alternative versions of the *n*th *Taylor approximation* for $f(x)$ centred on $x = a$. They are also known as *Taylor polynomials*. (A Maclaurin approximation is a special case of a Taylor approximation, obtained by putting $a = 0$.)

ACTIVITY

Explain the connection between the first Taylor approximation for $f(x)$ and the Newton–Raphson method of approximating to the root of the equation $f(x) = 0$.

Historical note

The Taylor approximations were discovered or rediscovered in various forms by several mathematicians in the seventeenth and eighteenth centuries. They were familiar to Scotsman James Gregory (1638–1675), though Englishman Brook Taylor (1685–1731) was the first to publish an account of them, in 1715. In 1742 Colin Maclaurin (1698–1745), Gregory's successor as professor at Edinburgh, published his expansion, stating that it occurred as a special case of Taylor's result; for some reason it has been credited to him as a separate theorem.

EXERCISE 6C

1 Use known Maclaurin series to find the Maclaurin series for each of the following functions as far as the term in x^4.

  (i) $\sin 3x$ **(ii)** $\cos 2x$

  (iii) $\sin^2 x$ **(iv)** $\ln(1 + \sin x)$

  (v) $\dfrac{\cosh x}{\sqrt{1 + x^2}}$ **(vi)** $e^{\sin x}$

2 Write down the first three terms of the expansion of $(1 + x^2)^{-\frac{1}{2}}$ when $|x| < 1$. Hence, or otherwise, obtain the series expansion for $\operatorname{arsinh} x$, as far as the term in x^5.

                                                                        [MEI, part]

3 **(i)** Find $\displaystyle\int \dfrac{1}{\sqrt{1 - 4x^2}}\,dx$.

  (ii) By expanding $(1 - 4x^2)^{-\frac{1}{2}}$ and integrating term by term, or otherwise, find the series expansion for $\arcsin(2x)$, when $|x| < \frac{1}{2}$, as far as the term in x^7.

                                                                         [MEI, part]

4 **(i)** By integrating $\dfrac{1}{1 + x^2}$ and its Maclaurin expansion, show that the Maclaurin series for $\arctan x$ is

$$x - \frac{x^3}{3} + \frac{x^5}{5} - \frac{x^7}{7} + \cdots.$$

    (This is known as Gregory's series, after the Scottish mathematician James Gregory; who published it in 1668, well before Newton or Leibniz introduced calculus. The series is valid for $|x| \leqslant 1$.)

  (ii) By putting $x = 1$ show that

$$\frac{\pi}{4} = 1 - \frac{1}{3} + \frac{1}{5} - \frac{1}{7} + \cdots.$$

    (This is known as Leibniz's series. It converges very slowly.)

  (iii) Show that

    (a) $\dfrac{\pi}{4} = \arctan \dfrac{1}{2} + \arctan \dfrac{1}{3}$ (known as Euler's formula for π)

    (b) $\dfrac{\pi}{4} = 4 \arctan \dfrac{1}{5} - \arctan \dfrac{1}{239}$ (known as Machin's formula).

  (iv) Use Machin's formula together with Gregory's series to find the value of π to 5 decimal places. (In 1873 William Shanks used this method to calculate π to 707 decimal places, but he made a mistake in the 528th place, not discovered until 1946!)

5 (i) Sketch the graph of $y = \arccos(2x)$.

(ii) Differentiate $\arccos(2x)$ with respect to x.

(iii) Use integration by parts to find $\int \arccos(2x)\,\mathrm{d}x$.

(iv) By first expanding $(1 - 4x^2)^{-\frac{1}{2}}$, find the series expansion of $\arccos(2x)$ as far as the term in x^5.

[MEI, part]

6 (i) Show that $\cosh^4 x = \frac{1}{8}\cosh 4x + \frac{1}{2}\cosh 2x + \frac{3}{8}$.

(ii) Find the series expansion for $\cosh^4 x$, as far as the term in x^4.

[MEI, part]

7 (i) Prove by induction that

$$f(x) = e^x \sin x \Rightarrow f^{(n)}(x) = 2^{n/2}\, e^x \sin\left(x + \frac{n\pi}{4}\right).$$

Use this result to obtain the Maclaurin series for $e^x \sin x$ as far as x^6.

(ii) Multiply the third Maclaurin approximation for e^x by the third Maclaurin approximation for $\sin x$, and comment on your answer.

(iii) Find a Maclaurin approximation for $e^x \cos x$ by multiplying the third Maclaurin approximation for e^x by the fourth Maclaurin approximation for $\cos x$, giving as many terms in your answer as you think justifiable.

8 Let $y = \arctan x$, so that $x = \tan y$.

(i) Using $\cos y = \frac{1}{2}(e^{jy} + e^{-jy})$ and $\sin y = \frac{1}{2j}(e^{jy} - e^{-jy})$, prove that $x = \dfrac{e^{2jy} - 1}{j(e^{2jy} + 1)}$.

(ii) By solving **(i)** for y, deduce that $y = \dfrac{1}{2j}(\ln(1 + jx) - \ln(1 - jx))$.

(iii) Use the Maclaurin series for $\ln(1 \pm t)$ in **(ii)** to obtain again Gregory's series for $\arctan x$.

9 A projectile is launched from O with initial velocity $\begin{pmatrix} u \\ v \end{pmatrix}$ relative to horizontal and vertical axes through O. The path of the projectile may be modelled in various ways. The table below shows the position (x, y) of the projectile at time t after launch, as given by two different models. Both models assume that g (gravitational acceleration) is constant. Use the Maclaurin expansion for e^{-kt}, where k is constant, to show that the results given by Model 1 are a special case of the results from Model 2, with $k = 0$.

	Assumptions about air resistance	Position at time t
Model 1	There is no air resistance.	$x = ut$ $y = vt - \frac{1}{2}gt^2$
Model 2	Air resistance is proportional to the velocity (with proportionality constant k).	$x = \frac{u}{k}(1 - e^{-kt})$ $y = \frac{g + kv}{k^2}(1 - e^{-kt}) - \frac{gt}{k}$

There are many ways of obtaining sequences of polynomial approximations for $f(x) \equiv \sin x$, for $0 \leqslant x \leqslant \frac{\pi}{2}$. Investigate alternative methods such as the following.

(i) Use **(a)** the linear function which passes through $(0, 0)$ and $\left(\frac{\pi}{2}, 1\right)$;

(b) the quadratic function which passes through $(0, 0)$, $\left(\frac{\pi}{4}, \frac{1}{\sqrt{2}}\right)$ and $\left(\frac{\pi}{2}, 1\right)$;

(c) the cubic function which passes through four points on $y = f(x)$; and so on.

(ii) Use polynomials $P(x)$ which minimise

(a) $\int_0^{\frac{\pi}{2}} (f(x) - P(x))\, dx$

(b) the maximum value of $|f(x) - P(x)|$ in $0 \leqslant x \leqslant \frac{\pi}{2}$

(c) $\int_0^{\frac{\pi}{2}} |f(x) - P(x)|\, dx$

(d) $\int_0^{\frac{\pi}{2}} (f(x) - P(x))^2\, dx.$

KEY POINTS

Maclaurin series

1 General form:

$$f(x) = f(0) + xf'(0) + \frac{x^2}{2!}f''(0) + \frac{x^3}{3!}f^{(3)}(0) + \cdots + \frac{x^r}{r!}f^{(r)}(0) + \cdots$$

2 Valid for all x:
$$e^x = 1 + x + \frac{x^2}{2!} + \frac{x^3}{3!} + \cdots + \frac{x^r}{r!} + \cdots$$

$$\sin x = x - \frac{x^3}{3!} + \frac{x^5}{5!} - \frac{x^7}{7!} + \cdots + \frac{(-1)^r x^{2r+1}}{(2r+1)!} + \cdots$$

$$\cos x = 1 - \frac{x^2}{2!} + \frac{x^4}{4!} - \frac{x^6}{6!} + \cdots + \frac{(-1)^r x^{2r}}{(2r)!} + \cdots$$

$$\sinh x = x + \frac{x^3}{3!} + \frac{x^5}{5!} + \frac{x^7}{7!} + \cdots + \frac{x^{2r+1}}{(2r+1)!} + \cdots$$

$$\cosh x = 1 + \frac{x^2}{2!} + \frac{x^4}{4!} + \frac{x^6}{6!} + \cdots + \frac{x^{2r}}{(2r)!} + \cdots$$

3 Valid for $|x| \leqslant 1$: $\quad \arctan x = x - \frac{x^3}{3} + \frac{x^5}{5} - \frac{x^7}{7} + \cdots + \frac{(-1)^{r-1}x^{2r-1}}{2r-1} + \cdots$

4 Valid for $|x| < 1$: $\quad \text{artanh}\, x = x + \frac{x^3}{3} + \frac{x^5}{5} + \frac{x^7}{7} + \cdots + \frac{x^{2r-1}}{2r-1} + \cdots$

5 Valid for $-1 < x \leqslant 1$: $\ln(1 + x) = x - \frac{x^2}{2} + \frac{x^3}{3} - \cdots + \frac{(-1)^{r-1}x^r}{r} + \cdots$

6 Validity depends on n:

$$(1 + x)^n = 1 + nx + \frac{n(n-1)}{2!}x^2 + \cdots + \frac{n(n-1)\ldots(n-r+1)}{r!}x^r + \cdots$$

If n is a positive integer: the series terminates after $n + 1$ terms, and is valid for all x.

If n is not a positive integer: the series is valid for $|x| < 1$; also for $|x| = 1$ if $n \geqslant -1$; and for $x = -1$ if $n > 0$.

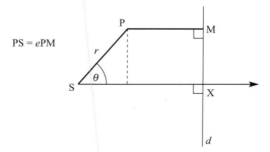

7 Conics 2

Will the line stretch out to the crack of doom?

William Shakespeare, 1564–1616

The polar equation of a conic

In Chapter 5 you met three types of conic, the parabola, the ellipse and the hyperbola. You saw that all of them have the focus–directrix property, but with different ranges of values for *e*. This observation leads to the following general definition of a conic.

> A *conic* is the locus of a point in a plane such that its distance from a fixed point S is a constant multiple of its distance from a fixed line *d*, both S and *d* being in the plane.

As before, the fixed point is called the *focus*, the fixed line is the *directrix*, and the constant multiplier is the *eccentricity*, denoted by *e*. If P is a point of the conic and M is the foot of the perpendicular from P to *d* then this focus–directrix definition says that SP = *e*PM.

Historical note

The conventional use of the letter S (initial of *solus* = 'sun' in Latin) to denote the focus is due to Kepler who discovered that the orbits of the planets are ellipses with the sun at one focus.

PS = *e*PM

Figure 7.1

This leads immediately to the polar equation of a conic. Take the focus S as the pole, and the perpendicular SX from S to the directrix *d* as the initial line (as in figure 7.1). Then

P lies on the conic $\quad\Leftrightarrow\quad$ SP $= e$PM

$\qquad\qquad\qquad\quad\Leftrightarrow\quad r = e(\text{SX} - r\cos\theta)$

$\qquad\qquad\qquad\quad\Leftrightarrow\quad r(1 + e\cos\theta) = e\text{SX}$

$\qquad\qquad\qquad\quad\Leftrightarrow\quad \dfrac{\ell}{r} = 1 + e\cos\theta,$ where ℓ is the constant eSX.

The constant ℓ has a simple geometrical meaning: when $\theta = \dfrac{\pi}{2}$, $\cos\theta = 0$ and so $r = \ell$.

The chord of the conic through the focus and parallel to the directrix is called the *latus rectum* ('upright side'), so ℓ is the length of the semi-latus rectum (see figure 7.2)

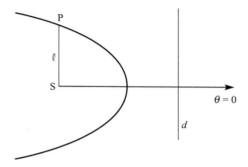

Figure 7.2

The polar equation can be rearranged to give

$$r = \frac{\ell}{1 + e\cos\theta},$$

which in turn shows again that there are three distinct types of conic, depending on the size of e.

1 If $0 < e < 1$ then the denominator $1 + e\cos\theta$ is never zero, so r remains finite, giving a closed curve, an *ellipse*.

2 If $e = 1$ then the denominator is zero when $\theta = \pi$, so that r can be made arbitrarily large as θ approaches π. The conic is a curve open towards the $\theta = \pi$ direction, a *parabola*.

3 If $e > 1$ then $1 + e\cos\theta = 0$ when $\cos\theta = -\dfrac{1}{e}$. This gives two values of θ for which r is undefined, and a range of values for which r is negative. The conic has two branches, and is called a *hyperbola*. Figure 2.6 on page 30 shows one hyperbola in detail.

These three types of conic are shown in figure 7.3.

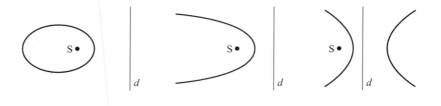

(a) Ellipse, $e < 1$ **(b)** Parabola, $e = 1$ **(c)** Hyperbola, $e > 1$

Figure 7.3

EXERCISE 7A   *Throughout this exercise **C** is the conic with polar equation $\dfrac{\ell}{r} = 1 + e\cos\theta$.*

1 By plotting points or using a graphic calculator or computer, draw separate sketch graphs of **C** when $\ell = 5$ and

    (i) $e = \frac{1}{3}$ **(ii)** $e = \frac{1}{2}$
    (iii) $e = 1$ **(iv)** $e = 2$
    (v) $e = 3$.

2 Prove that the distance from the focus to the directrix is $\dfrac{\ell}{e}$ and add the directrix to each of your sketches in Question 1. Show that the polar equation of the directrix can be put in the form $\dfrac{\ell}{r} = e\cos\theta$.

3 A family of conics all have a common focus and directrix. Sketch on a single diagram the members of this family for which

    (i) $e = \frac{1}{3}$ **(ii)** $e = \frac{1}{2}$
    (iii) $e = 1$ **(iv)** $e = 2$
    (v) $e = 3$.

4 Describe **C** **(i)** when $e = 0$ **(ii)** when e is very large.

5 A conic has polar equation $\dfrac{5a}{r} = 3 + 2\cos\theta$.

    (i)   Find the eccentricity of the conic, and state what type of conic it is.
    (ii)   Sketch the conic. Given that one focus of the conic is at the origin, find the polar co-ordinates of the other focus.

                                                                [MEI, part]

6 In polar co-ordinates (r, θ) two conics C_1 and C_2 have equations

$$\frac{a}{r} = 1 + \cos\theta \qquad \text{and} \qquad \frac{4a}{r} = 3 + 2\cos\theta.$$

    (i)   Find the polar co-ordinates of the two points where C_1 and C_2 intersect.
    (ii)   Sketch C_1 and C_2 on the same diagram, giving a clear indication of the scale.
                                                               [MEI, part]

7 Prove that the polar equation of the parabola can be written in the form

$$r = \frac{\ell}{2} \sec^2 \frac{\theta}{2}.$$

8 In polar co-ordinates with origin O, a conic has equation $\dfrac{2a}{r} = 2 + \cos\theta$.

   (i) State what type of conic it is, and sketch the curve.

   (ii) Two points P and Q on the conic are such that the line PQ passes through the origin.

     Show that $\dfrac{1}{OP} + \dfrac{1}{OQ} = \dfrac{2}{a}$.

                                                     [MEI, part]

9 The chords PQ, UV of a parabola or an ellipse are perpendicular focal chords.

   Prove that $\dfrac{1}{PQ} + \dfrac{1}{UV} = \dfrac{2 - e^2}{2\ell}$.

10 **(i)** Prove that $\dfrac{\ell}{r} = \cos(\theta - \alpha) + e\cos\theta$ is the polar equation of a straight line.

       [**Hint**: Convert to cartesian co-ordinates.]

   (ii) Show that this line meets C where $\theta = \alpha$ and nowhere else.

   (iii) Deduce that this line is the tangent to C at the point where $\theta = \alpha$.

11 Prove that the tangents at the end of a focal chord meet on the directrix.

12 The tangents from a point T to C touch C at H and K.

   Prove that angle TSH = angle TSK, where S is the focus.

13 A curve Q has polar equation $r = a(1 + 2\cos\theta)$ for $-\frac{2}{3}\pi \leqslant \theta \leqslant \frac{2}{3}\pi$.

   (i) Sketch the curve Q.

   (ii) Find the area of the region enclosed by the curve Q.

   Another curve H has polar equation $\dfrac{a}{r} = 1 + 2\cos\theta$, for $-\frac{2}{3}\pi \leqslant \theta \leqslant \frac{2}{3}\pi$. This is part of a conic, with the origin O as a focus.

   (iii) Write down the eccentricity of the conic.

   (iv) Sketch the curve H (on a separate diagram).

   (v) Draw in the directrix of the conic corresponding to the focus O, and find the equation of this directrix in the form $r\cos\theta = k$.

                                                         [MEI]

Focal distance and reflector properties

Focal distance properties

In Chapter 5 the focus–directrix definition PS = ePM was used for the parabola and the hyperbola, but the ellipse was defined differently, by S′P + SP = constant. So you now have two proposed definitions of an ellipse: 'sum of focal distances' from Chapter 5 and 'focus–directrix' from the previous section. To establish that these actually define the same curve you need to show that, with the usual notation,

$$PS = e\text{PM} \iff SP + S'P = \text{constant}.$$

One half of this ($\Longleftarrow$) has been done in Chapter 5 (page 98). The converse argument starts by showing that PS = ePM with $e < 1$ gives a curve with a second focus and directrix. This is done exactly as for the hyperbola on page 105, except that since $e^2 - 1$ is now negative it is better to let $b^2 = a^2(1 - e^2)$, leading to $\dfrac{x^2}{a^2} + \dfrac{y^2}{b^2} = 1$.

| ACTIVITY

Write out the argument on page 105 in full for the case $e < 1$.

The rest follows immediately.

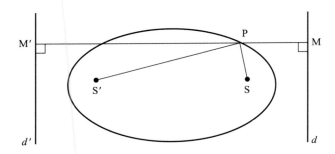

Figure 7.4

With the notation of figure 7.4

$$SP = e\text{PM} \qquad \text{and} \qquad S'P = e\text{PM}'$$

$$\Longrightarrow \qquad SP + S'P = e(\text{PM} + \text{PM}')$$
$$= e\text{MM}'$$
$$= e \times \frac{2a}{e}$$
$$= 2a.$$

Therefore $PS = e\text{PM} \Longrightarrow SP + S'P = 2a = \text{constant}.$

The other central conic, the hyperbola, has a corresponding property. This is proved in a similar way, but now the length MM' is the *difference* of the lengths PM and PM', so

> the difference of the distances from the foci to any point of a hyperbola is constant, and equals the length of the transverse axis.

| ACTIVITY

Prove this in detail, by drawing the diagram for the hyperbola corresponding to figure 7.4 and showing that S'P – SP = 2a for points P on one branch, and SP – S'P = 2a for points on the other branch.

This property of hyperbolas is the basis of many modern navigation systems. Two radio beacons S, S' transmit simultaneous radio pulses, which arrive at a ship P at slightly different times (unless SP = S'P). By measuring this time lag (electronically) the difference SP – S'P can be calculated; the locus of points for which SP – S'P takes this value is one branch of a particular hyperbola with foci S, S'. By using the same procedure with pulses from S and a third beacon S" the ship can also be located on one branch of a second hyperbola with foci S, S" (see figure 7.5). The intersection of these two branches gives the position of the ship, which can be found either from a specially drawn chart showing families of hyperbolas or by computer.

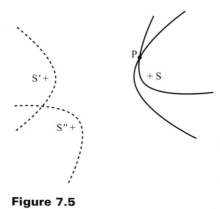

Figure 7.5

 This method can be extended to fix positions in three dimensions (for example to track a robot exploring the sea bed). Discuss how to do this.

Reflector properties

The *focal distance properties* (SP = PM for the parabola, SP + S'P = 2*a* for the ellipse, $|\text{SP} - \text{S'P}| = 2a$ for the hyperbola) lead via a simple argument first used by Roberval in 1634 to the *reflector properties*. His idea was to consider a curve to be the path of a moving point P, so that the direction of the tangent at P is the direction of the velocity of P. Dealing first with the parabola, since PS and PM are always equal they must change at the same rate, so P must be moving away from S and from the directrix at equal speeds. Therefore if the velocity **v** of P makes angles ϕ and ψ with SP and MP respectively (see figure 7.6) then $v \cos \phi = v \cos \psi$, and so $\phi = \psi$. This means that the tangent at P bisects angle SPM. (This has already been proved in Exercise 5A, Question 4.)

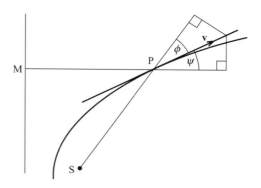

Figure 7.6

ACTIVITY

Prove that rays of light emitted from the focus and reflected by a parabolic mirror will produce a beam of light parallel to the axis, and that an incoming beam parallel to the axis will converge at the focus (= 'hearth' in Latin). Give some practical applications of this.

For the ellipse SP + S'P is constant, so the rate of increase of SP equals the rate of decrease of S'P. The velocity **v** of P has equal resolved parts in the directions of $\overrightarrow{SP}$ and $\overrightarrow{PS'}$, i.e. $v\cos\phi = v\cos\psi$ (see figure 7.7), and therefore $\phi = \psi$. This means that the tangent at P is equally inclined to SP and S'P.

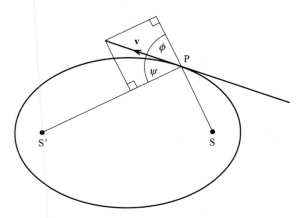

Figure 7.7

ACTIVITY

Prove by a similar method that the tangent at a point P of a hyperbola is equally inclined to the focal lines SP and S'P.

The reflector property of the ellipse is used in a modern medical device called a *lithotripter* (= 'stone crusher') (see figure 7.8). This directs a powerful high frequency beam of sound waves at a kidney stone, so that the stone breaks into small fragments which pass from the body naturally. The sound source is at one focus of an elliptical mirror which is placed so that the stone is at the other focus. The beam spreads out from the source and then converges at the stone, which is thus the only part of the patient to receive the full effect of the beam. This prevents the sound waves from damaging the surrounding tissue.

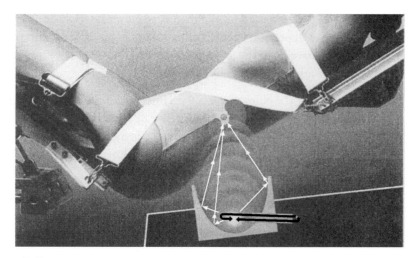

Figure 7.8

1 Check the property SP + S′P = 2a for the ellipse of figure 7.7 by direct measurement from the diagram for several positions of P. Check similarly the corresponding property of the hyperbola from figure 5.13.

2 A variable circle passes through a fixed point S and touches a fixed straight line d. Prove that the locus of its centre is a parabola.

3 The diagram below shows a straight rod S′K of length ℓ which is pivoted at the point S′. A piece of string of length s (< ℓ) has one end fastened at a fixed point S and the other at K. If the string is kept taut by a pencil P held against the rod, show that the locus of P is part of a hyperbola with transverse axis of length ℓ − s.

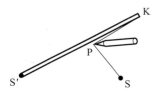

4 P(at^2, 2at) is a general point on the parabola $y^2 = 4ax$.

(i) Find the equation of the tangent to the parabola at P, and the equation of the normal to the parabola at P.

The tangent meets the x axis at T, and the normal meets the x axis at N. F is the point (a, 0) and D is the point (−a, 2at).

(ii) Draw a diagram showing the parabola and the points P, T, N, F and D.

(iii) Find the co-ordinates of T and N, and show that F is the mid-point of TN.

(iv) Deduce (or prove otherwise) that FP = FT and that PT bisects the angle FPD.

[MEI]

5 An ellipse (shown below) has equation $\dfrac{x^2}{a^2} + \dfrac{y^2}{b^2} = 1$ and eccentricity e, where a, b, e are positive constants and $b^2 = a^2(1 - e^2)$. The foci of the ellipse are $F(ae, 0)$ and $G(-ae, 0)$. The point $P(x_1, y_1)$ lies on the ellipse.

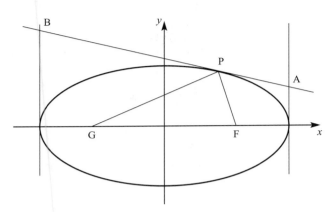

(i) Find the gradient of the ellipse at the point P in terms of a, b, x_1 and y_1. Hence show that the equation of the tangent at P is $\dfrac{xx_1}{a^2} + \dfrac{yy_1}{b^2} = 1$.

(ii) The tangent at P meets the line $x = a$ at $A(a, p)$ and meets the line $x = -a$ at $B(-a, q)$. Find p and q, and show that $pq = b^2$.

(iii) Write down the equation of the directrix corresponding to the focus F. Show that $PF = a - ex_1$, and find a similar expression for PG.

(iv) Now suppose that angle FPG is a right angle. By applying Pythagoras' theorem, or otherwise, show that $x_1^2 = a^2\left(2 - \dfrac{1}{e^2}\right)$. Find the range of values of e for which this is possible.

(v) For the case when angle FPG is a right angle, state, with a reason, the size of angle FPA.

[MEI]

6 A hyperbola has equation $\dfrac{x^2}{a^2} - \dfrac{y^2}{b^2} = 1$ and eccentricity e, where a, b and e are positive constants such that $b^2 = a^2(e^2 - 1)$.

(i) Find (in terms of a, b, x_1 and y_1) the gradient at the point (x_1, y_1) on the hyperbola, and hence show that the equation of the tangent at this point is $\dfrac{xx_1}{a^2} - \dfrac{yy_1}{b^2} = 1$.

(ii) Show that $P(ae, a(e^2 - 1))$ is a point on the hyperbola, and find the equation of the tangent at P, in a form not involving b.

The foci of the hyperbola are $S(ae, 0)$ and $S'(-ae, 0)$. The tangent at $P(ae, a(e^2 - 1))$ meets the x axis at D and the y axis at A. The straight line PS' meets the y axis at T.

(iii) Draw a diagram showing the hyperbola and the points S, S', P, D, A and T.

(iv) Show that D lies on a directrix of the hyperbola.

(v) Show that $TA = TP$. [*You may assume the reflection property if you wish.*]

[MEI]

7 The variable circle C with centre P touches two fixed circles C_1 and C_2 with centres A_1 and A_2 respectively. Prove that if C_1 lies entirely outside C_2 then the locus of P is both branches of a hyperbola with foci A_1, A_2.

Find the locus of P **(i)** if C_1 lies entirely inside C_2 **(ii)** if C_1 and C_2 intersect.

8 It is proposed to build a straight motorway connecting two towns A and B which are 200 km apart. In a rough model to investigate the effect this would have on the surrounding area it is assumed that traffic moves at 100 km/h on the motorway and at 50 km/h elsewhere, and that it is possible to drive directly to A or to B from any other point.

Taking cartesian co-ordinates so that A and B are $(-100, 0)$ and $(100, 0)$ respectively, find the set of points which would benefit from the motorway in the sense that to drive to A via B and the motorway would be quicker than driving directly to A.

9 (i) The diagram shows a *crossed parallelogram linkage* in which A and B are fixed points, and BC, CD, DA are movable rods with AB = CD, BC = AD and AB < BC. The rods BC and AD cross at P; prove that the locus of P is an ellipse with foci A and B.

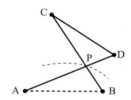

[**Hint**: Consider the symmetry of the figure.]

(ii) The next diagram shows a system of *elliptical gears*, consisting of the ellipse of part **(i)** fixed to a shaft at A together with a congruent ellipse with foci C, D fixed to a shaft at D, so that A and D are now fixed, and both ellipses can rotate. The two gears are kept in contact by the rod BC, and have a common tangent at P.

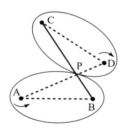

As the ellipse AB is made to turn, it drives the ellipse CD, but the effective radii of the two gears, AP and DP, vary continuously, so that a constant speed input produces a variable speed output: this is used to provide a 'slow feed, quick return' mechanism in a number of machines. Prove that if the angular speed of ellipse AB is the constant ω then the angular speed of ellipse CD varies from $\dfrac{1-e}{1+e}\omega$ to $\dfrac{1+e}{1-e}\omega$.

10 Alternative proofs of the reflector properties

(i) The point P of the ellipse $\dfrac{x^2}{a^2} + \dfrac{y^2}{b^2} = 1$ has co-ordinates $(a\cos\theta, b\sin\theta)$.

Prove that the vector $\mathbf{t} = \begin{pmatrix} -a\sin\theta \\ b\cos\theta \end{pmatrix}$ is in the direction of the tangent at P.

(ii) Let $\overrightarrow{SP} = \mathbf{u}$ and $\overrightarrow{PS'} = \mathbf{v}$, where S and S' are the foci. Prove that $|\mathbf{u}| = a(1 - e\cos\theta)$ and $|\mathbf{v}| = a(1 + e\cos\theta)$, and deduce that the vector $(1 + e\cos\theta)\mathbf{u} + (1 - e\cos\theta)\mathbf{v}$ is in the direction of the external bisector of angle SPS'.

(iii) Hence show that SP and S'P are equally inclined to the tangent at P.

(iv) Prove the reflector property of the hyperbola by a similar method.

11 (i) Given two fixed points S and S' in a plane, use the focal distance properties to prove that through every other point of the plane there passes a unique ellipse with foci S, S' and (except for points on the perpendicular bisector of SS') a unique hyperbola with foci S, S'. This set of ellipses and hyperbolas is said to form a *confocal system*.

(ii) Use the reflector properties to prove that, in a confocal system, each ellipse meets each hyperbola *orthogonally*, i.e. that the tangents at the intersection are perpendicular. Sketch a confocal system to show this.

(iii) Describe the system of orthogonal curves which is obtained in the limit as $SS' \to 0$.

The conics as sections of a cone

The parabola, ellipse and hyperbola are called conics (or conic sections) because they were originally studied as plane sections of a right circular cone.

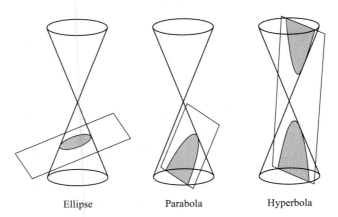

Ellipse   Parabola   Hyperbola

Figure 7.9

Figure 7.9 shows a double cone standing with its axis vertical. A horizontal plane not through the vertex cuts the cone in a circle. When the plane is tilted slightly the section is an ellipse. As the angle of tilt increases the section becomes more elongated until, when the plane is parallel to a generator of the cone (i.e. a straight line through the vertex in the surface of the cone), the section is a parabola. With further tilting, the plane cuts the other half of the cone too, and the section is a hyperbola. So the parabola is the borderline case, separating ellipses from hyperbolas.

❓ Is it possible to obtain ellipses of all shapes and sizes as the sections of a single cone? Is the same true of hyperbolas?

Historical note

In 1525 the German artist Albrecht Dürer (1471–1528) published a treatise on perspective and geometry which included drawing sections of a cone by using measurements from its plan and elevation. His ellipse (see figure 7.10) is particularly interesting since he was convinced that the curve should widen in proportion with the widening of the cone, so he distorted the ellipse into an 'eierlinie' ('egg line', i.e. 'oval'). This error (by a master draughtsman with exceptionally acute perception) shows that it is necessary to *prove* that the sections of a cone are exactly the same as the curves produced from the focus–directrix definition. An elegant way of doing this, devised by Germinal Dandelin in 1822, is given in Question 1 of the next exercise.

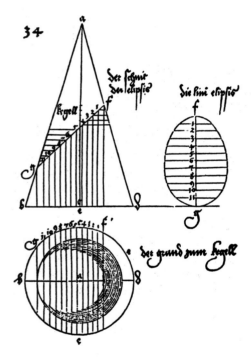

Figure 7.10

EXERCISE 7C

Most of this exercise refers to the diagram on the next page, which shows a plane Π cutting a cone with vertex V and a vertical axis. Any generator of the cone makes angle α with the vertical, and Π is inclined at angle β to the vertical. Between Π and V there is just one sphere which touches the cone and Π (to see this, imagine a tiny sphere touching the inside of the cone near V and then growing until it also touches Π). This *Dandelin sphere* touches Π at S and touches the cone in a horizontal circle. The horizontal plane containing this circle meets Π in the line *d*. From any point P of the conic section perpendiculars are drawn meeting *d* at M and meeting the horizontal plane at N. The generator PV meets the circle of contact at Q.

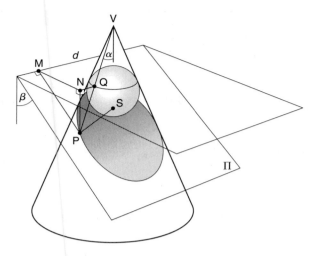

1 Prove the following properties of this figure.

   (i) $PS = PQ$.

   (ii) $\angle NPQ = \alpha$.

   (iii) $PN = PS \cos \alpha$.

   (iv) $\angle NPM = \beta$.

   (v) $PN = PM \cos \beta$.

   (vi) $PS = \dfrac{\cos \beta}{\cos \alpha} PM$.

   (vii) P lies on the conic with focus S, directrix d, and eccentricity $\dfrac{\cos \beta}{\cos \alpha}$.

   (viii) This conic is an ellipse if $\beta > \alpha$, a parabola if $\beta = \alpha$, and a hyperbola if $\beta < \alpha$.

2 Show that in the cases of the ellipse and hyperbola there is a second Dandelin sphere touching the cone and Π, and describe its position in each case. Explain why the point S′ where this touches Π is the other focus of the conic.

3 Prove the focal distance properties ($SP + S'P = 2a$ for the ellipse, $|\,SP - S'P\,| = 2a$ for the hyperbola) directly from the Dandelin figure.

4 Show that the co-ordinates (x, y, z) of a point on the line joining the points

   (x_0, y_0, z_0) and (f, g, h) are given by $\begin{pmatrix} x \\ y \\ z \end{pmatrix} = \begin{pmatrix} f \\ g \\ h \end{pmatrix} + \lambda \begin{pmatrix} x_0 - f \\ y_0 - g \\ z_0 - h \end{pmatrix}$.

   Deduce that the cone which passes through the ellipse $\dfrac{x^2}{a^2} + \dfrac{y^2}{b^2} = 1$, $z = 0$ and has its vertex at (f, g, h), $h \neq 0$, has the equation

   $$\frac{(fz - hx)^2}{a^2} + \frac{(gz - hy)^2}{b^2} = (z - h)^2.$$

   What is the significance of the condition $h \neq 0$?

   Show that this cone meets the plane $x = 0$ in a circle if the vertex lies on a certain hyperbola in the plane $y = 0$.

   [MEI]

5 An ellipse has major axis AA′ and foci S, S′. Prove that the locus of viewing points from which this ellipse is seen as a circle is the hyperbola with transverse axis SS′ and foci A, A′ in the plane perpendicular to the plane of the ellipse.

PROJECTILE TRAJECTORIES

(i) A particle is thrown from the origin O with initial velocity $\binom{u}{v}$ referred to horizontal and vertical axes. Its position vector after time t is

$$\binom{x}{y} = \binom{ut}{vt - \frac{1}{2}gt^2},$$ where g is the acceleration due to gravity. Show that the cartesian equation of its trajectory (path) can be written as

$$\left(x - \frac{uv}{g}\right)^2 = -\frac{2u^2}{g}\left(y - \frac{v^2}{2g}\right).$$

Deduce that the trajectory is a parabola, and find the co-ordinates of its focus and the length of its semi-latus rectum.

(ii) Show that the directrix of this parabola is $y = \dfrac{V^2}{2g}$, where $V = \sqrt{u^2 + v^2}$ is the initial speed. Note that the position of the directrix is independent of the angle of projection.

(iii) Show that if the particle is thrown vertically upward it will just reach the directrix.

(iv) Now suppose that the particle is thrown with speed V from a point O on a sloping plane so as to hit the plane at a point B further up the line of greatest slope through O.

Explain the following construction for the possible trajectories (figure 7.11):

Draw the directrix at height $\dfrac{V^2}{2g}$ above O, and construct circles with centres O and B to touch this. Then the points S_1 and S_2 where these circles intersect are the foci of the two possible parabolic trajectories.

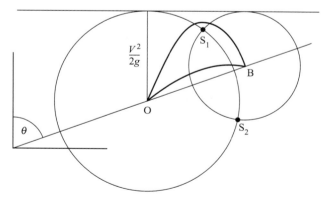

Figure 7.11

(v) By considering what happens as B moves up the slope, prove that
   (a) the greatest range up the slope occurs when the focus of the trajectory lies on the slope
   (b) the direction of projection then bisects the angle between OB and the vertical
   (c) the direction of motion at B is then perpendicular to the direction of motion at O.

(vi) Show that the greatest range r up the slope is given by $r = \dfrac{V^2}{g(1 + \cos\theta)}$, where θ is the angle between the slope and the vertical.

(vii) By letting θ vary, show that the set of points which the particle can hit when thrown from O with initial speed V is bounded by a parabola (called the *parabola of safety*). Describe the corresponding set of points in three dimensions.

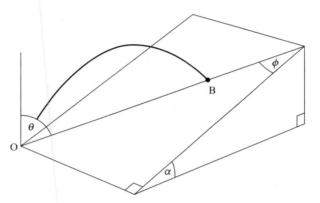

Figure 7.12

(viii) Finally suppose that the particle is thrown from a point O on a plane which is inclined at an angle α to the horizontal, hitting the plane at B, where OB makes an angle ϕ with the line of greatest slope OA and an angle θ with the vertical (see figure 7.12).

Show that $\cos\theta = \sin\alpha\cos\phi$. Deduce that the set of points on the plane which the particle can hit is bounded by an ellipse with one focus at O and eccentricity $\sin\alpha$.

1 A conic can be expressed in polar co-ordinates (with the origin as the focus) as:

$$\frac{\ell}{r} = 1 + e\cos\theta$$

where ℓ is the length of the semi-latus rectum and e is the eccentricity.

2 Focal distance properties: SP + S'P = $2a$ for ellipse,

$\left| \text{SP} - \text{S'P} \right| = 2a$ for hyperbola.

3 Reflector properties:

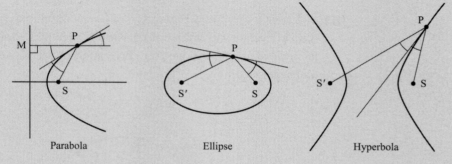

Parabola   Ellipse   Hyperbola

4 The conics may be obtained as plane sections of a circular cone. If the cone has a vertical axis and semi-vertical angle α, and the cutting plane is inclined to the vertical at angle β then the eccentricity of the conic section is $\dfrac{\cos\beta}{\cos\alpha}$.

Appendix: Functions of a complex variable

This appendix is included to give you a glimpse of how some of the ideas in this book can be brought together and taken a little further. All the necessary tools are available from earlier chapters, but this work goes beyond the scope of the current examination specification.

From your knowledge of multiplying and dividing complex numbers you are familiar with polynomial and rational functions of a complex variable z, and on page 43 you met the definition

$$e^z = e^x(\cos y + j \sin y), \text{ where } z = x + jy.$$

From this come the familiar results

$$e^{j\theta} = \cos \theta + j \sin \theta \quad \text{and} \quad e^{-j\theta} = \cos \theta - j \sin \theta$$

and hence

$$\cos \theta = \frac{e^{j\theta} + e^{-j\theta}}{2} \quad \text{and} \quad \sin \theta = \frac{e^{j\theta} - e^{-j\theta}}{2j} \text{ (see page 44).}$$

These suggest the following definitions for the circular functions of a complex variable:

$$\cos z = \frac{e^{jz} + e^{-jz}}{2} \quad \text{and} \quad \sin z = \frac{e^{jz} - e^{-jz}}{2j}.$$

From page 76 it is natural to give similar definitions for the hyperbolic functions:

$$\cosh z = \frac{e^z + e^{-z}}{2} \quad \text{and} \quad \sinh z = \frac{e^z - e^{-z}}{2}.$$

Other circular and hyperbolic functions are defined as usual:

$$\sec z = \frac{1}{\cos z}, \quad \tanh z = \frac{\sinh z}{\cosh z}, \text{ etc.}$$

ACTIVITY

Prove from these definitions that these four functions are periodic, with $\cos z$ and $\sin z$ having period 2π and $\cosh z$ and $\sinh z$ having period $2\pi j$.

ACTIVITY

Prove Euler's formulae:

(i) $\cos jz = \cosh z$

(ii) $\sin jz = j \sinh z$

(iii) $\cosh jz = \cos z$

(iv) $\sinh jz = j \sin z$.

The results of the last activity make it possible to find the real and imaginary parts of these trigonometric or hyperbolic functions. For example

$$\cos z = \cos(x + jy) = \cos x \cos jy - \sin x \sin jy$$
$$= \cos x \cosh y - j \sin x \sinh y.$$

This in turn enables you to solve problems which until now have seemed impossible, as in the following example.

EXAMPLE

Solve the equation $\cos z = 5$.

SOLUTION

$$\cos(x + jy) = 5 \iff \cos x \cosh y - j \sin x \sinh y = 5$$
$$\iff \cos x \cosh y = 5 \quad \text{and} \quad \sin x \sinh y = 0.$$
$$\text{Now } \sin x \sinh y = 0 \iff \sin x = 0 \quad \text{or} \quad \sinh y = 0.$$

If $\sinh y = 0$ then $y = 0$, so $\cosh y = 1$ and $\cos x = 5$, which is impossible since x is real.

If $\sin x = 0$ then $x = n\pi$, so $\cos x = (-1)^n$ and $(-1)^n \cosh y = 5$.

This is impossible if n is odd, but if n is even it gives $\cosh y = 5$, so $y = \pm\text{arcosh}\,5 \approx \pm 2.292$.

So the equation $\cos z = 5$ has infinitely many solutions, $z = 2k\pi \pm j\,\text{arcosh}\,5$. On an Argand diagram these give points spaced at intervals of 2π along the parallel lines $y \approx \pm 2.292$ (figure A.1).

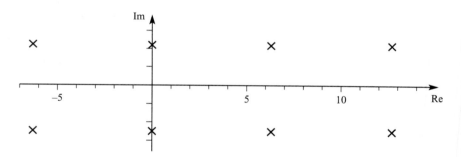

Figure A.1

This brings you to the threshold of the theory of functions of a complex variable, first studied systematically by Augustin-Louis Cauchy (1789–1857), which has proved to have many applications in other areas of pure mathematics, physics and engineering. This most fertile branch of mathematics has been called the mathematical joy of the nineteenth century.

1 Find the real and imaginary parts of $\cos(2 + 3j)$ and of $\cosh(2 + 3j)$, giving your answers correct to 3 decimal places.

2 Find the real and imaginary parts of $\sinh(x + jy)$.

3 Prove that $\cosh(j\pi - \theta) = -\cosh\theta$ and $\sinh\left(\dfrac{j\pi}{2} - \theta\right) = j\cosh\theta$.

4 **(i)** Prove from the definitions given on page 145 that
   (a) $\cos^2 z + \sin^2 z = 1$
   (b) $\sin(z + w) = \sin z \cos w + \cos z \sin w$ (start with the right-hand side).

   (ii) Prove similarly one other standard trigonometric formula of your choice.

5 Give definitions of $\tan z$ and $\tanh z$ for the complex number z. What can be deduced about the periodicity of these functions?

6 Given that $w = \sin(x + jy)$

   (i) find $\operatorname{Re}(w)$ and $\operatorname{Im}(w)$
   (ii) prove that $|w|^2 = \frac{1}{2}(\cosh 2y - \cos 2x)$
   (iii) prove that $\tan(\arg w) = \cot x \tanh y$.

7 Find z if $\cosh z = -1$.

8 Prove that if $h > 1$ then:
$$\sin z = h \Leftrightarrow z = (2k + \tfrac{1}{2})\pi \pm j\operatorname{arcosh} h.$$
State the corresponding result if $h < -1$.

9 Using horizontal x and y axes and a vertical h axis, describe and sketch the set of points (x, y, h) for which $\cos z = h$, where h is real and $z = x + jy$.

10 Prove that $w = \ln|z| + j\arg z$ is one solution of the equation $e^w = z$, and find all the other solutions in terms of z. The given solution is called the *principal logarithm* of z, and is written $\ln z$.

11 Find the principal logarithm of

   (i) -1 **(ii)** j
   (iii) $-5j$ **(iv)** $4 + 3j$.

12 A complex power of a non-zero complex number is defined as follows:
$$z^w = e^{w\ln z} \ (z \neq 0).$$
Prove that j^j is real, and find its value to 3 significant figures.

13 Working to 3 significant figures, find

   (i) 1^j **(ii)** $(-1)^j$
   (iii) $(1 - j)^{1+j}$ **(iv)** $(1 + 2j)^{3+4j}$.

14 Describe the motion of the point representing z^j in an Argand diagram as the point representing z moves once clockwise around the unit circle, starting at -1.

The point representing the complex number z in an Argand diagram (called the z plane) is mapped to the point representing the complex number w in a second Argand diagram (the w plane), where $w = f(z)$. As z moves along a straight line $\text{Re}(z) = h$ in the z plane so w moves along a curve in the w plane. The set of such curves for different real values of h is called Family A. Similarly, Family B is the set of curves in the w plane which are the images of the lines $\text{Im}(z) = k$ for different real values of k.

(i) Show that if $f(z) = e^z$ then Family A consists of circles with centre at the origin, and Family B consists of half-lines radiating from the origin.

(ii) Show that if $f(z) = \cosh z$ then Family A consists of ellipses, Family B consists of hyperbolas, and all these conics are confocal (see page 139).

(iii) Investigate Family A and Family B for other functions $f(z)$ $\left(\text{for example, } z^2 \text{ or } \cos z \text{ or } \frac{1}{z}\right)$. If the working becomes intractable, consider using computer power to plot the curves.

(iv) Investigate the angles at which curves of Family A meet curves of Family B.

Answers

Chapter 1

❓ (Page 1)

Each cuboid in Figure 1.1(b) has a side of length $x - y$. The products of the remaining sides give the terms x^2, xy and y^2.

Activity (Page 2)

(i) **(a)** and **(b)** The greater of m and n **(c)** $m + n$
(ii) **(a)** and **(b)** Less than or equal to m **(c)** $2m$

Exercise 1A (Page 4)

1 $x^2 + 2x + 1 \equiv (x + 3)(x - 1) + 4$

2 $x^3 + 4x^2 - 7x + 2 \equiv (x + 3)(x^2 + x - 10) + 32$

3 $x^4 + 6x^2 + 12 \equiv (x - 5)(x^3 + 5x^2 + 31x + 155) + 787$

4 $2x^3 + 3x^2 - 5x + 7 \equiv (2x + 1)(x^2 + x - 3) + 10$

5 **(i)** $2x^4 - 3x^2 - 5x + 7 \equiv (x^2 + 2)(2x^2 - 7) - 5x + 21$
(ii) $4x^5 - 2x^4 - 2x^3 + x^2 - 3x + 2$
$\equiv (2x^2 - 3)(2x^3 - x^2 + 2x - 1) + 3x - 1$
(iii) $x^4 + 2x^3 - 5x^2 + 4x + 9$
$\equiv (x^2 + x + 3)(x^2 + 3x - 5) - 10x + 24$
(iv) $3x^4 - 8x^3 + 29x^2 + 21$
$\equiv (x^2 - x + 7)(3x^2 - 5x + 3) + 38x$
(v) $x^4 + 3x - 1 \equiv (x^2 - 2)(x^2 + 2) + 3x + 3$
(vi) $x^4 - 1 \equiv (x - 1)(x^3 + x^2 + x + 1)$

6 **(i)** **(a)** $x^2 - a^2 \equiv (x - a)(x + a)$
(b) $x^3 - a^3 \equiv (x - a)(x^2 + ax + a^2)$
(c) $x^4 - a^4 \equiv (x - a)(x^3 + ax^2 + a^2x + a^3)$
(ii) $x^{n-1} + ax^{n-2} + a^2x^{n-3} + \cdots + a^{n-2}x + a^{n-1}$ is a geometric series with first term x^{n-1} and common ratio $\frac{a}{x}$. Its sum is

$$\frac{x^{n-1}\left(1 - \left(\frac{a}{x}\right)^n\right)}{1 - \frac{a}{x}} = \frac{x^{n-1} - \frac{a^n}{x}}{1 - \frac{a}{x}} = \frac{x^n - a^n}{x - a}.$$

The result follows.

7 **(ii)** $x^3 + a^3 \equiv (x + a)(x^2 - ax + a^2)$
$x^5 + a^5 \equiv (x + a)(x^4 - ax^3 + a^2x^2 - a^3x + a^4)$

8 5

9 4

10 $16x + 33$

11 $r = 1, s = 5$

Exercise 1B (Page 7)

1 **(i)** -2 **(ii)** -2 **(iii)** 1 **(iv)** 13 **(v)** -5

2 **(i)** 0 **(ii)** 0 **(iii)** 0 **(iv)** -12 **(v)** 12

3 $a = 8$, $b = 1$, $c = -42$; solutions $-3, -7, 2$

4 **(i)** $P(a)$ **(ii)** -7 **(iii)** 6 **(iv)** -3
(v) $g(2) = f'(2) = -48$

5 **(i)** -183 **(ii)** 6

7 $P(x) \equiv 0 \Leftrightarrow a = b = c = 0;$
$P(x) = 0 \Leftrightarrow x = \dfrac{-b \pm \sqrt{b^2 - 4ac}}{2a}$ provided that $a \neq 0$.

9 $r = \dfrac{P(a) - P(b)}{a - b}, \ s = \dfrac{aP(b) - bP(a)}{a - b}$

11 **(ii)** RS

12 **(i)** $r = -5, s = 17$ **(ii)** $10x - 13$

13 **(i)** **(a)** -1 **(b)** 7 **(ii)** $-12x + 37$ **(iii)** $-28x + 85$

❓ (Page 10)

(i) No **(ii)** No

Exercise 1C (Page 11)

1 $a = 1, b = 4, c = 4$

2 $a = 1, b = -3, c = 3, d = -1$

3 $a = -4, b = 2, c = 2$

5 **(i)** There are infinitely many possible values of a, b, c:
$a = 2 + c, b = -1 - 2c$
(ii) Unique values of a, b, c: $a = 3, b = -3, c = 1$
(iii) There are no such values of a, b, c

6 $a = b = \pm 2, c = 2$

7 **(iii)** $y = \dfrac{A(x - b)(x - c)(x - d)}{(a - b)(a - c)(a - d)} + \dfrac{B(x - c)(x - d)(x - a)}{(b - c)(b - d)(b - a)}$

$+ \dfrac{C(x - d)(x - a)(x - b)}{(c - d)(c - a)(c - b)} + \dfrac{D(x - a)(x - b)(x - c)}{(d - a)(d - b)(d - c)}$

8 (i) $y = 3x^2 - 5x + 3$ **(ii)** $y = x^3 - 3x^2 + 2x + 1$

9 $h(x) = \frac{9}{4}x^2 - 6x + \frac{23}{4}$

❓ (Page 12)

$f(x) = 0$ and $f'(x) = 0$ have a common root, 2.

Exercise 1D (Page 13)

1 $x = 4$ (repeated), $x = 2$

2 $x = 6$ (repeated), $x = 3$

3 $x = -3$ (repeated), $x = \frac{1}{2}$

4 $x = \frac{1}{3}$ (repeated), $x = -5$

5 $x = -\frac{3}{2}$ (repeated), $x = 3$

6 $x = -1$ (occurs three times), $x = 2$

7 $x = -1$ (repeated), $x = -2$ (repeated)

8 $f(x) = 0$ and $f^{(n-1)}(x) = 0$ share a root, where $f^{(n-1)}(x) \equiv (n-1)$th derivative of $f(x)$

Activity (Page 15)

You get back to the original equation.

Exercise 1E (Page 15)

1 (i) $-\frac{7}{2}, 3$ **(ii)** $\frac{1}{5}, -\frac{1}{5}$ **(iii)** $0, \frac{2}{7}$

(iv) $-\frac{24}{5}, 0$ **(v)** $-11, -4$ **(vi)** $-\frac{8}{3}, -2$

2 (i) $z^2 - 10z + 21 = 0$
 (ii) $2z^2 + 19z + 45 = 0$
 (iii) $z^2 - 5z = 0$
 (iv) $z^2 - 6z + 9 = 0$
 (v) $z^2 - 6z + 13 = 0$

3 (i) $2, 3, \frac{2}{3}, \frac{1}{3}$
 (ii) $3z^2 - 2z + 1 = 0$
 (iii) $cz^2 + bz + a = 0$

4 (i) $2z^2 - 5z - 9 = 0$
 (ii) $2z^2 + 15z + 16 = 0$
 (iii) $4z^2 - 61z + 81 = 0$
 (iv) $18z^2 + 61z + 18 = 0$

5 $z^2 - 16z - 8 = 0$

6 (i) $az^2 + bkz + ck^2 = 0$
 (ii) $az^2 + (b - 2ka)z + (k^2a - kb + c) = 0$

7 (i) Distinct negative (real) roots
 (ii) $\alpha = -\beta$
 (iii) One root is 0
 (iv) Distinct real roots, one positive, the other negative

9 (i) $3x^2 - 6x - (11 + k) = 0$;   1;
  locus of M is the vertical line $x = 1$.
 (ii) Locus of M is the vertical line $x = \dfrac{m - b}{2a}$.

Activity (Page 17)

(i) $(\alpha + \beta + \gamma)^2 \equiv \alpha^2 + \beta^2 + \gamma^2 + 2(\alpha\beta + \beta\gamma + \gamma\alpha)$

(ii) $\alpha\beta\gamma \left(\frac{1}{\alpha} + \frac{1}{\beta} + \frac{1}{\gamma} \right) \equiv \alpha\beta + \beta\gamma + \gamma\alpha$

(ii) $\alpha^3 + \beta^3 + \gamma^3 - 3\alpha\beta\gamma$
  $\equiv (\alpha + \beta + \gamma)(\alpha^2 + \beta^2 + \gamma^2 - \alpha\beta - \beta\gamma - \gamma\alpha)$

The proofs are by direct expansion and simplification.

Activity (Page 18)

$z = -\dfrac{d}{aw} \Longleftrightarrow w = -\dfrac{d}{az} = \dfrac{\alpha\beta\gamma}{z}$, since $-\dfrac{d}{a} = \alpha\beta\gamma$.

So w takes the values $\beta\gamma, \gamma\alpha, \alpha\beta$ as z takes the values α, β, γ.

The equation simplifies to $a^2w^3 - acw^2 + bdw - d^2 = 0$.

Suppose that α (say) is 0. Then $d = -\alpha\beta\gamma a = 0$ and the equation becomes

$$a^2w^3 - acw^2 = 0$$
$$\Longleftrightarrow aw^2(aw - c) = 0$$
$$\Longleftrightarrow w = 0 \text{ (twice) or } \frac{c}{a}$$
$$= 0 \text{ (twice) or } \beta\gamma, \text{ since } \frac{c}{a} = \alpha\beta + \beta\gamma + \gamma\alpha \text{ and } \alpha = 0$$
$$= \alpha\beta, \beta\gamma, \gamma\alpha \text{ with } \alpha = 0.$$

Exercise 1F (Page 18)

1 (i) $-\frac{3}{2}$ **(ii)** $-\frac{1}{2}$ **(iii)** $-\frac{7}{2}$ **(iv)** $\frac{13}{4}$

(v) $-\frac{129}{8}$ **(vi)** $\frac{497}{16}$ **(vii)** $\frac{1}{7}$ **(viii)** $\frac{3}{7}$

(ix) $\frac{45}{4}$ **(x)** $-\frac{45}{14}$

2 (i) $z^3 - 8z^2 - 4z + 24 = 0$
 (ii) $z^3 - 10z^2 + 27z - 19 = 0$
 (iii) $z^3 - 8z^2 + 15z + 1 = 0$

3 (i) $2, 5, 8$
 (ii) $-\frac{2}{3}, \frac{2}{3}, 2$
 (iii) $2 - 2\sqrt{3}, 2, 2 + 2\sqrt{3}$
 (iv) $\frac{2}{3}, \frac{7}{6}, \frac{5}{3}$

4 $1.5, 2, 2.5; k = 23.5$

5 $-0.75, 0.25, 0.5$

6 (i) $a^2z^3 + (2ac - b^2)z^2 + (c^2 - 2bd)z - d^2 = 0$
(ii) $d^2z^3 - (c^2 - 2bd)z^2 - (2ac - b^2)z - a^2 = 0$
(iii) $a^2dz^3 - a(2bd - c^2)z^2 + d(b^2 - 2ac)z + ad^2 = 0$

7 $ac^3 = db^3$; 0.5, 1.5, 4.5

8 (i) 5, −6, 4
(ii) 37
(iv) $z^3 + z^2 + 37z - 4 = 0$

9 $p = 7, q = 8, \alpha = -1$; or $p = q = \alpha = 0$

10 $\frac{7}{3}, \frac{3}{7}, -2$

11 $\pm\sqrt{-q}, -p$

12 (i) $\frac{3}{2}, -6, 2$
(ii) $\frac{57}{4}, 30$
(iv) $2y^3 - 15y^2 + 24y + 7 = 0$

13 (i) $0, -\frac{27}{16}; k = -16(\alpha + \beta + \gamma)$
(ii) $-\frac{3}{4}, \frac{3}{2}, \frac{3}{2}; k = -36$
(iii) $27y^3 - 81y^2 + 90y - 20 = 0$

Exercise 1G (Page 21)

1 (i) $-\frac{15}{4}$ **(ii)** $\frac{3}{4}$ **(iii)** −12   **(iv)** $\frac{135}{8}$

3 (i) (a) −8   **(b)** 24   **(c)** −4   **(d)** 6
(ii) $y^4 - 4y^2 + 4 = 0$
(iii) $y = \pm\sqrt{2}$ (repeated), $x = \pm\sqrt{2} - 2$ (repeated)

5 (i) $\alpha = -\frac{2}{3}, \beta = \frac{2}{\sqrt{3}}$
(ii) −16
(iii) $9y^3 - 48y^2 + 72y - 32 = 0$

6 (i) (a) 0   **(b)** $-\frac{2}{3}$ **(c)** 6   **(d)** −3
(ii) $4y^4 + 69y^2 - 54y + 9 = 0$
(iii) 0; $\alpha, \beta, \gamma, \delta$ are not all real.

7 (i) $k = -24, m = 16$
(iii) $y^2 - 6y - 81 = 0$
(iv) $\alpha + \beta = 3(1 + \sqrt{10}), \gamma + \delta = 3(1 - \sqrt{10})$
(v) $\beta^2 - 3(1 + \sqrt{10})\beta + 4 = 0,$
$\gamma^2 - 3(1 - \sqrt{10})\gamma + 4 = 0,$
$\delta^2 - 3(1 - \sqrt{10})\delta + 4 = 0$

Chapter 2

Activity (Page 25)
E.g. $\left(6, -\frac{\pi}{4}\right), \left(6, \frac{7\pi}{4}\right), \left(-6, -\frac{5\pi}{4}\right)$

Exercise 2A (Page 26)

1 Kite

2 (i) $\left(4, \frac{11\pi}{12}\right)$ and $\left(4, -\frac{5\pi}{12}\right)$
(ii) $\left(4, \frac{7\pi}{12}\right)$ or $\left(4, -\frac{\pi}{12}\right)$
(iii) $\left(\frac{4}{\sqrt{3}}, \frac{3\pi}{4}\right)$ and $\left(\frac{4}{\sqrt{3}}, -\frac{\pi}{4}\right)$, or $\left(4, -\frac{3\pi}{4}\right)$ and $\left(4\sqrt{3}, \frac{3\pi}{4}\right)$, or $\left(4, -\frac{3\pi}{4}\right)$ and $\left(4\sqrt{3}, -\frac{\pi}{4}\right)$

3 (ii) A(5.39, 0.38), B(8.71, 1.01), C(8.71, 1.64), D(5.39, 2.27)
(iii) B(4.64, 7.37), C(−0.58, 8.69), D(−3.45, 4.14)

4 (i) 4
(ii) $16 < r < 170, \theta = -27$
(iii) (a) $99 < r < 107, 153 < \theta < 171$
(b) $16 < r < 99$ or $107 < r < 162, -81 < \theta < -63$
(c) $16 < r < 99$ or $107 < r < 162,$
$45 < \theta < 63$ or $162 < r < 170, 153 < \theta < 135$ or $99 < r < 107, -9 < \theta < 9$

❓ (Page 29)

This uses $x = r\cos\theta, y = r\sin\theta$, with $r = f(\theta)$.

Exercise 2B (Page 30)

1 $x^2 + y^2 - 8y = 0$

2

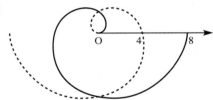

3 (i) Circle
(ii)

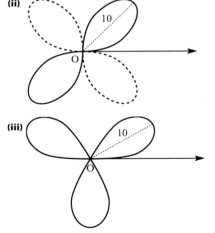

(iii)

(iv) n repeated petals when n is odd, $2n$ petals when n is even

4

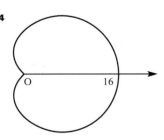

5 $x = a$, $y = b$

6 $x \cos \alpha + y \sin \alpha = p$

7 $\left(a, \pm\frac{\pi}{3}\right)$, $\quad 2r = a \sec \theta$

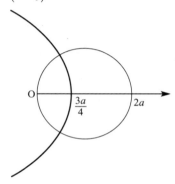

? **(Page 32)**

(a) $\delta\theta < 0$, $\delta r < 0$, $\delta A < 0$,
$\frac{1}{2}(r + \delta r)^2(-\delta\theta) < -\delta A < \frac{1}{2}r^2(-\delta\theta)$

(b) $\delta\theta > 0$, $\delta r < 0$, $\delta A > 0$,
$\frac{1}{2}(r + \delta r)^2\delta\theta < \delta A < \frac{1}{2}r^2\delta\theta$

(c) $\delta\theta < 0$, $\delta r > 0$, $\delta A < 0$,
$\frac{1}{2}r^2(-\delta\theta) < -\delta A < \frac{1}{2}(r + \delta r)^2(-\delta\theta)$

In all cases $\frac{\delta A}{\delta\theta}$ is between $\frac{1}{2}r^2$ and $\frac{1}{2}(r + \delta r)^2$, so the limiting argument holds as before.

Activity (Page 33)

(i) $2\pi + \dfrac{3\sqrt{3}}{2}$ 　　　　 (ii) $\pi + 3\sqrt{3}$

Exercise 2C (Page 33)

1 It gives twice the area.

2 $\dfrac{64\pi}{3}$

3 $24\pi \pm 64$

4 $e^{4k\pi}$

5 $\dfrac{a^2}{2}$

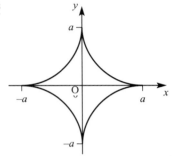

6 $\dfrac{5\pi a^2}{4}$

8 3.1

9 $\dfrac{3\pi a^2}{8}$

11 (i)

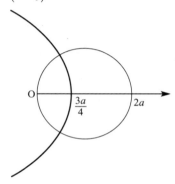

(ii) $\frac{1}{12}\pi a^2$

(iii) Polar $\left(\frac{a}{\sqrt{2}}, \frac{\pi}{4}\right)$, cartesian $\left(\frac{1}{2}a, \frac{1}{2}a\right)$

(iv) $4x^3 + 4xy^2 + 4x^2y\dfrac{dy}{dx} + 4y^3\dfrac{dy}{dx}$
$= 6axy + 3ax^2\dfrac{dy}{dx} - 3ay^2\dfrac{dy}{dx}$

(v) $\dfrac{dy}{dx} = \frac{1}{2}$

12 (i)

(ii) 2

(iv) $4x^3 + 4xy^2 + 4x^2y\dfrac{dy}{dx} + 4y^3\dfrac{dy}{dx} - 8x + 8y\dfrac{dy}{dx} = 0$

(vi) $\left(\sqrt{2}, \pm\frac{\pi}{6}\right)$

Chapter 3

Exercise 3A (Page 39)

1 (i) $\dfrac{1 - j}{\sqrt{2}}$ 　　　 (ii) $-\dfrac{1 + \sqrt{3}j}{2}$

(iii) $-\dfrac{\sqrt{3} + j}{2}$ 　　　 (iv) $\dfrac{-1 + j}{\sqrt{2}}$

2 (i) $-8 + 8\sqrt{3}j = -8 + 13.856j$

(ii) $-1024 - 1024j$

(iii) $-0.078 + 0.997j$

(iv) -46656

3 (i) $\cos 8\alpha - j\sin 8\alpha$

(ii) $\cos 2\beta - j\sin 2\beta$

(iii) $\cos^{10}\gamma(\cos 10\gamma + j\sin 10\gamma)$

(iv) $\dfrac{\cos 4\delta - j\sin 4\delta}{16\cos^4\delta}$

Activity (Page 40)

(ii) $16\sin^5\theta - 20\sin^3\theta + 5\sin\theta$

Activity (Page 41)

$\dfrac{\sin 5\theta - 5\sin 3\theta + 10\sin\theta}{16}$

Exercise 3B (Page 41)

1 $\dfrac{4t - 4t^3}{1 - 6t^2 + t^4}$, where $t = \tan\theta$

2 (i) $c^3 - 3cs^2 = 4c^3 - 3c$

(ii) $3c^2s - s^3 = 3s - 4s^3$

(iii) $\dfrac{3t - t^3}{1 - 3t^2}$ where $c = \cos\theta$, $s = \sin\theta$ and $t = \tan\theta$

3 $32c^6 - 48c^4 + 18c^2 - 1$, $32c^5 - 32c^3 + 6c$, where $c = \cos\theta$

4 $\dfrac{{}^nC_1 t - {}^nC_3 t^3 + \cdots}{1 - {}^nC_2 t^2 + {}^nC_4 t^4 - \cdots}$

5 (i) $\dfrac{\cos 4\theta + 4\cos 2\theta + 3}{8}$

(ii) $\dfrac{\sin 5\theta - 5\sin 3\theta + 10\sin\theta}{16}$

(iii) $\dfrac{-\cos 6\theta + 6\cos 4\theta - 15\cos 2\theta + 10}{32}$

(iv) $\dfrac{\cos 7\theta - \cos 5\theta - 3\cos 3\theta + 3\cos\theta}{64}$

(v) $\dfrac{-\sin 7\theta - \sin 5\theta + 3\sin 3\theta + 3\sin\theta}{64}$

7 (i) $-\frac{1}{192}\sin 6\theta + \frac{3}{64}\sin 4\theta - \frac{15}{64}\sin 2\theta + \frac{5}{16}\theta + k$

(ii) $\frac{2}{35}$

(iii) $\frac{4}{35}$

8 $\dfrac{\sin 2n\theta}{2\sin\theta}$

9 (i) $\cos n\theta + j\sin n\theta$, $\cos n\theta - j\sin n\theta$, $2\cos n\theta$, $2j\sin n\theta$

(iii) $p = \frac{1}{16}$, $q = \frac{1}{32}$, $r = -\frac{1}{16}$, $s = -\frac{1}{32}$

10 (i) Same as 9 **(i)**

(ii) $p = \frac{1}{16}$, $q = -\frac{1}{32}$, $r = -\frac{1}{16}$, $s = \frac{1}{32}$

11 0

Activity (Page 44)

$e^{z+2\pi nj} = e^z \times e^{2\pi nj} = e^z(\cos 2\pi n + j\sin 2\pi n) = e^z \times 1.$

Exercise 3C (Page 45)

1 (i) -1

(ii) $\dfrac{1+j}{\sqrt{2}}$

(iii) $-1.209 + 0.698j$

(iv) $-13.129 + 15.201j$

2 $3 + 2k\pi j$

3 $-4 + \left(2k - \frac{1}{3}\right)\pi j$

4 All z

6 Rhombus

9 $\dot z = (\dot r + jr\dot\theta)e^{j\theta}$, $\ddot z = (\ddot r - r\dot\theta^2 + j(2\dot r\dot\theta + r\ddot\theta))e^{j\theta}$,
where the dot shows differentiation with respect to t.
Components:

	radial	transverse
velocity	$\dot r$	$r\dot\theta$
acceleration	$\ddot r - r\dot\theta^2$	$2\dot r\dot\theta + r\ddot\theta$

10 $C = \dfrac{e^{3x}(3\cos 2x + 2\sin 2x)}{13} + c$,

$S = \dfrac{e^{3x}(-2\cos 2x + 3\sin 2x)}{13} + c'$

11 $\dfrac{e^{ax}(a\cos bx + b\sin bx)}{a^2 + b^2} + c$, $\dfrac{e^{ax}(-b\cos bx + a\sin bx)}{a^2 + b^2} + c'$

Activity (Page 46)

$S = 2^n \cos^n\dfrac{\theta}{2}\sin\dfrac{n\theta}{2}$

Exercise 3D (Page 47)

1 $\dfrac{\sin\theta + \sin(n-1)\theta - \sin n\theta}{2 - 2\cos\theta}$

2 (iii) $\displaystyle\sum_{r=0}^{n} {}^nC_r 2^{n-r}\sin\dfrac{2r\pi}{3} = 3^{n/2}\sin\dfrac{n\pi}{6}$

3 (i) $\cos k\theta + j\sin k\theta$, $\cos k\theta - j\sin k\theta$

(ii) $|w| = \sin\theta$, $\arg w = \theta - \dfrac{\pi}{2}$

Square roots have modulus $\sqrt{\sin\theta}$ and arguments $\dfrac{\theta}{2} - \dfrac{\pi}{4}$, $\dfrac{\theta}{2} + \dfrac{3\pi}{4}$.

(iii) $\dfrac{e^{j\theta}\cos\theta(1 - (e^{j\theta}\cos\theta)^n)}{1 - e^{j\theta}\cos\theta}$

(iv) $\dfrac{\cos\theta - \cos n\theta\cos^{n+1}\theta}{\sin\theta}$

4 (i) $\cos 2\theta + j\sin 2\theta$, $\cos 3\theta + j\sin 3\theta$, $\cos n\theta + j\sin n\theta$

(ii) $1 + \dfrac{z}{3} + \dfrac{z^2}{9} + \dfrac{z^3}{27} + \cdots + \dfrac{z^n}{3^n} + \cdots$

(iii) $\dfrac{3}{3-z}$

(iv) (a) $C = \dfrac{9 - 3\cos\theta}{10 - 6\cos\theta}$ **(b)** $S = \dfrac{3\sin\theta}{10 - 6\cos\theta}$

5 (i) $\cos\theta + j\sin\theta$, $\cos n\theta + j\sin n\theta$, $\cos n\theta - j\sin n\theta$

(iv) $C = \dfrac{2\cos\theta}{5 - 4\cos 2\theta}$, $S = \dfrac{6\sin\theta}{5 - 4\cos 2\theta}$

6 (i) $\cos n\theta + j\sin n\theta$

(ii) $\cos\theta$, $\dfrac{5}{4} + \cos\theta$

(iv) $C = \dfrac{2\cos\theta + 1}{5 + 4\cos\theta}$, $S = \dfrac{2\sin\theta}{5 + 4\cos\theta}$

7 $2^n \cos^n\dfrac{\beta}{2}\,\sin\!\left(\alpha + \dfrac{n\beta}{2}\right)$

Activity (Page 48)

(i) ± 1

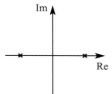

(ii) 1, $\dfrac{-1 \pm \sqrt{3}j}{2}$

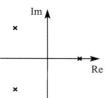

(iii) ± 1, $\pm j$

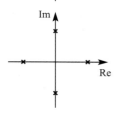

Activity (Page 49)

$\omega^r(\omega^r)^* = |\omega^r|^2 = 1 = \omega^n$. Therefore $(\omega^r)^* = \dfrac{\omega^n}{\omega^r} = \omega^{n-r}$.

Activity (Page 50)

The degree of the equation is now $n - 1$, since the $(jz)^n$ and $(-jz)^n$ terms now cancel. The working is the same, except that $\alpha + 1 = 0$ is now possible, when $k = \dfrac{n}{2}$. So the $n - 1$ roots are $z = \tan\dfrac{k\pi}{n}$, $k = 0, 1, 2, \ldots, n - 1$, $k \neq \dfrac{n}{2}$.

Exercise 3E (Page 50)

1 The fifth roots give alternate tenth roots, and their negatives (given by half turn about O) fill the gaps.

3 $-\alpha$, $\pm\alpha\omega$, $\pm\alpha\omega^2$

5 (iv) If and only if m and n have no common factor

6 $\dfrac{j}{2}$, $\dfrac{\pm\sqrt{3} + j}{2}$

7 $\cos\dfrac{k\pi}{3} + j\sin\dfrac{k\pi}{3}$, $k = 1, 2, 3, 4, 5$

9 $\dfrac{\cos\dfrac{2k\pi}{n}}{1 - \sin\dfrac{2k\pi}{n}}$, $k = 0, 1, 2, \ldots, n - 1$

(excluding $k = \dfrac{3n}{4}$ if n is a multiple of 4)

10 $\cot\dfrac{(2k + 1)\pi}{2n}$, $k = 0, 1, 2, \ldots, n - 1$

Activity (Page 52)

$1.22 + 0.19j$

❓ (page 53)

$\sqrt{-1}$ is ambiguous, meaning j at one stage and $-$j at another.

Exercise 3F (Page 53)

1 $\pm(0.90 + 2.79j)$

2 ± 1, $\pm j$

3 $-119 - 120j$, $-3 + 2j$, $-2 - 3j$, $3 - 2j$

4

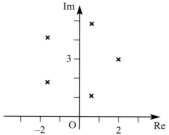

5 $(z + 1 - 3j)^7 = 2187$

7 Regular n-gon with one vertex at O

9 (i) $2 + 2j$, $-2 + 2j$, $-2 - 2j$, $2 - 2j$

(ii)

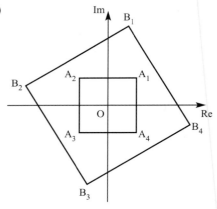

(iii) Rotate (centre O) through $+\frac{\pi}{6}$ and enlarge $\times 2$.
$B_1B_2 = 8$.

(iv) $512 - 512\sqrt{3}j$

10 (i) $e^{j\theta} = \cos\theta + j\sin\theta$, $e^{-j\theta} = \cos\theta - j\sin\theta$

(ii) $2e^{j\alpha}$, where $\alpha = \pm\frac{\pi}{5}, \pm\frac{3\pi}{5}, \pi$

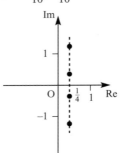

(iii) $\beta = \pm\frac{\pi}{10}, \pm\frac{3\pi}{10}$

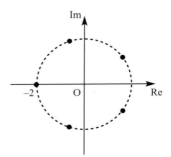

11 (i) $\cos k\theta + j\sin k\theta$, $\cos k\theta - j\sin k\theta$

(ii) $\sqrt{2}e^{j\theta}$, where $\theta = \frac{\pi}{12}, \frac{5\pi}{12}, \frac{3\pi}{4}, -\frac{\pi}{4}, -\frac{7\pi}{12}, -\frac{11\pi}{12}$

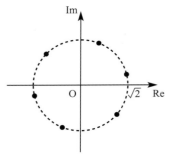

(iii) $-1 + j, 1 - j$

(iv) $p = \frac{1}{2\sqrt{2}}$, $\alpha = \frac{\pi}{24}, \frac{5\pi}{24}, \frac{3\pi}{8}, -\frac{\pi}{8}, -\frac{7\pi}{24}, -\frac{11\pi}{24}$

13 (i) $8\left(\cos\frac{\pi}{10} + j\sin\frac{\pi}{10}\right)$

(ii) $\frac{1}{49}\left(\cos-\frac{\pi}{4} + j\sin-\frac{\pi}{4}\right)$

(iii) $\frac{1}{2187}\left(\cos\frac{7\pi}{12} + j\sin\frac{7\pi}{12}\right)$

14 (i) $\frac{-1+j}{\sqrt{2}}, \frac{1-j}{\sqrt{2}}$, $(j^{1/2})^3 = j^{3/2}$

(ii) Both $\frac{1 + \sqrt{3}j}{2}$

(iii) $-\pi < m\arg w < \pi$

15 (i) $\cos k\theta + j\sin k\theta$, $\cos k\theta - j\sin k\theta$

(ii) $\frac{e^{j\theta}(1 - e^{2nj\theta})}{1 - e^{2j\theta}}$, which simplifies to $\frac{\sin n\theta}{\sin\theta}e^{jn\theta}$ by using result **(i)**.

(iii) $\arg(C + jS) = n\theta$

(iv) $C = \frac{\sin n\theta \cos n\theta}{\sin\theta}$, $S = \frac{\sin^2 n\theta}{\sin\theta}$

(v) Let the side $A_{n-1}A_n$ be represented by the complex number w_n ($n = 1, 2, ..., 6$).
Then $|w_n| = 1$ (unit sides)

and

$\arg(w_n) = \frac{\pi}{7} + (n - 1)\frac{2\pi}{7}$
(each external angle of the heptagon is $\frac{2\pi}{7}$)

$= \frac{(2n - 1)\pi}{7}$.

So $w_n = e^{(2n-1)j\pi/7}$ and $z_n = w_1 + w_2 + ... + w_n$

(by vector addition round the heptagon from O).

$\arg(z_n) = \frac{1}{7}n\pi$ follows from **(iii)** with $\theta = \frac{\pi}{7}$.

16 He was essentially right, in the sense that by replacing $\sqrt{-1}$ by j and ∞ by n, and then letting $n \to \infty$ gives the limit π.

Activity (Page 57)

$$\arg\left(\frac{a-b}{c-b}\right) = \arg(a-b) - \arg(c-b)$$

$$= \angle XBA - \angle XBC = \angle ABC$$

Activity (Page 58)

$$\arg\left(\frac{z+3}{z-2j}\right) = \frac{2\pi}{3}$$

Activity (Page 58)

The argument is as in Example 3.11, with the extra step of taking the conjugate which reflects triangle DEF to produce opposite similarity.

Exercise 3G (Page 60)

2

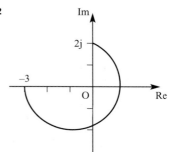

3

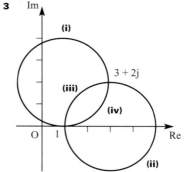

4 Converse is not true.

5 (i)

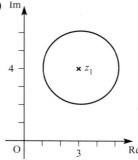

(ii)

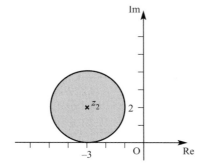

(iii)

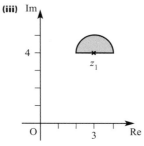

(iv)

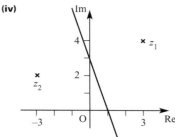

(v)

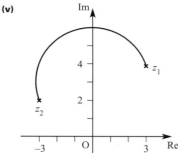

(vi) $3x^2 + 3y^2 + 30x - 8y + 27 = 0$

Circle centre $\left(-5, \frac{4}{3}\right)$, radius $\frac{4\sqrt{10}}{3}$

6 $ae^{*} + bf^{*} + cd^{*} = af^{*} + bd^{*} + ce^{*}$

8 (i) Vector ωz is vector z turned through $\frac{2\pi}{3}$.

    (ii) $3 - 2\sqrt{3} + (5 + \sqrt{3})j, \ 3 + 2\sqrt{3} + (5 - \sqrt{3})j$

13 (ii) Result is still true.

    (iii) Let D coincide with A. Then S also coincides with A.

Chapter 4

Activity (Page 67)

(i) The gradient is always negative.

(ii) $y = \arccos x \Rightarrow \cos y = x \Rightarrow -\sin y \dfrac{dy}{dx} = 1$

$$\Rightarrow \frac{dy}{dx} = \frac{-1}{\sin y} = \frac{-1}{\pm\sqrt{1 - \cos^2 y}} = \frac{-1}{\pm\sqrt{1 - x^2}}$$

Since $\dfrac{dy}{dx}$ is negative (from **(i)**), $\dfrac{dy}{dx} = -\dfrac{1}{\sqrt{1 - x^2}}$.

Activity (Page 67)

The graphs in figure 4.8 are obtained by reflecting the graphs in figure 4.7 in $y = x$.

The gradient is always positive, tending to 0 as $x \to \pm\infty$. Maximum gradient $= 1$, when $x = 0$.

$y = \arctan x \Rightarrow \tan y = x \Rightarrow$
$\sec^2 y \dfrac{dy}{dx} = 1 \Rightarrow \dfrac{dy}{dx} = \dfrac{1}{\sec^2 y} = \dfrac{1}{1 + \tan^2 y} = \dfrac{1}{1 + x^2}$.

Activity (Page 68)

(i) $y = \text{arcsec}\, x \Leftrightarrow \sec y = x \Leftrightarrow \dfrac{1}{\cos y} = x$

    $\Leftrightarrow \cos y = \dfrac{1}{x} \Leftrightarrow y = \arccos\left(\dfrac{1}{x}\right)$.

For **(ii)** and **(iii)** the argument is similar.

Exercise 4A (Page 69)

1

	arcsine	arccosine	arctangent
Domain	$-1 \leqslant x \leqslant 1$	$-1 \leqslant x \leqslant 1$	all real numbers
Range	$-\frac{\pi}{2} \leqslant y \leqslant \frac{\pi}{2}$	$0 \leqslant y \leqslant \pi$	$-\frac{\pi}{2} < y < \frac{\pi}{2}$

3 $\arccos x + \arccos(-x) = \pi$

4 $-\dfrac{\pi}{2} \leqslant x \leqslant \dfrac{\pi}{2}$

6 (i) $\dfrac{1}{\sqrt{1 - x^2}}$ **(ii)** $\dfrac{5}{\sqrt{1 - 25x^2}}$

    (iii) $\dfrac{6}{4 + 9x^2}$ **(iv)** $-\dfrac{3}{1 + (2 - 3x)^2}$

7 (i) $\dfrac{2}{\sqrt{1 - 4x^2}}$ **(ii)** $\dfrac{5}{1 + 25x^2}$

    (iii) $\dfrac{6x}{\sqrt{1 - 9x^4}}$ **(iv)** $-\dfrac{2}{\sqrt{1 - 4x^2}}$

    (v) $\dfrac{e^x}{1 + e^{2x}}$ **(vi)** $-\dfrac{2x}{1 + (1 - x^2)^2}$

    (vii) $-\dfrac{10x}{\sqrt{1 - (5x^2 - 2)^2}}$ **(viii)** $-\dfrac{1}{2\sqrt{x(1 - x)}}$

8 $\arcsin \dfrac{x}{\sqrt{2}} - \dfrac{\pi}{4}$

9 $\dfrac{1}{\sqrt{1 - x^2}}, -\dfrac{1}{\sqrt{1 - x^2}}; c_2 = \dfrac{\pi}{2} + c_1$

10 (i) $n\pi$ or $2n\pi \pm \dfrac{\pi}{3}$

    (ii) $2n\pi - \dfrac{\pi}{4}$

    (iii) $2n\pi \pm \dfrac{\pi}{3} + \arcsin \dfrac{4}{5}$

    (iv) $n\pi$ or $n\pi \pm \arctan \sqrt{\dfrac{1}{2}}$

    (v) $4n\pi$ or $4n\pi \pm \dfrac{4\pi}{3}$

    (vi) $(2n + 1)\pi$ or $2n\pi + 2\arcsin \dfrac{1}{\sqrt{5}}$

11

	arcsecant	arccosecant	arccotangent
Domain	$x \leqslant -1$ or $x \geqslant 1$	$x \leqslant -1$ or $x \geqslant 1$	all real numbers
Range	$0 \leqslant y \leqslant \pi,$ $y \neq \frac{\pi}{2}$	$-\frac{\pi}{2} \leqslant y \leqslant \frac{\pi}{2},$ $y \neq 0$	$-\frac{\pi}{2} < y \leqslant \frac{\pi}{2},$ $y \neq 0$

12 (ii) (a) $-\dfrac{1}{|x|\sqrt{x^2 - 1}}$ **(b)** $-\dfrac{1}{1 + x^2}$

13 (i) $\dfrac{\pi}{2}$ provided $x \leqslant -1$ or $x \geqslant 1$

    (ii) $-\dfrac{\pi}{2}$ if $x < 0$, $\dfrac{\pi}{2}$ if $x > 0$

Exercise 4B (Page 72)

1 (i) $\dfrac{1}{5}\arctan \dfrac{x}{5} + c$ **(ii)** $\arcsin \dfrac{x}{6} + c$

    (iii) $\dfrac{5}{6}\arctan \dfrac{x}{6} + c$ **(iv)** $\dfrac{2}{5}\arctan \dfrac{2x}{5} + c$

    (v) $\dfrac{1}{2}\arcsin \dfrac{2x}{3} + c$ **(vi)** $\dfrac{7}{\sqrt{3}}\arcsin \dfrac{\sqrt{3}x}{\sqrt{5}} + c$

2 (i) $\dfrac{\pi}{12}$ **(ii)** $\dfrac{\pi}{4}$

    (iii) $\dfrac{7\pi}{36}$ **(iv)** $\dfrac{\pi}{12}$

    (v) $\dfrac{\pi}{2\sqrt{6}}$ **(vi)** $\dfrac{\pi}{12\sqrt{10}}$

3 (i) $\dfrac{1}{12}\arctan \dfrac{4x}{3} + c$

❓ (Page 73)

No real roots $\Leftrightarrow B^2 - 4AC < 0$.

If $A < 0$, work with $\dfrac{-1}{-Ax^2 - Bx - C}$.

❓ (Page 74)

So that $Ax^2 + Bx + C$ can be rearranged as $p^2 - (qx + r)^2$.

Exercise 4C (Page 74)

1 (i) $\dfrac{1}{2}\arctan\dfrac{x+2}{2} + c$

(ii) $7\arcsin\dfrac{x-2}{3} + c$

(iii) $\dfrac{\sqrt{3}}{\sqrt{2}}\arctan\dfrac{\sqrt{2}x}{\sqrt{3}} + c$

(iv) $\dfrac{1}{2}\arctan\dfrac{3x+1}{2} + c$

(v) $\arcsin\dfrac{x-1}{2} + c$

(vi) $\dfrac{7}{2}\arcsin\dfrac{2x+1}{2} + c$

2 (i) $x\arcsin x + \sqrt{1-x^2} + c$

(ii) (a) $x\arccos x - \sqrt{1-x^2} + c$

   (b) $x\arctan x - \dfrac{1}{2}\ln(1+x^2) + c$

   (c) $x\,\mathrm{arccot}\,x + \dfrac{1}{2}\ln(1+x^2) + c$

3 (i) $\dfrac{1}{2}a^2\arcsin\dfrac{b}{a} + \dfrac{1}{2}b\sqrt{a^2-b^2}$

(ii) Area of sector + area of triangle

4 (i) $\dfrac{1}{2}\arctan\dfrac{x-3}{2} + c$

(ii) $\dfrac{1}{2}\arcsin\dfrac{2x+3}{4} + c$

(iii) $\dfrac{1}{4}\arctan\dfrac{2x+5}{2} + c$

(iv) $-\dfrac{1}{x-3} + c$

(v) $\dfrac{1}{3}\arcsin\dfrac{3x+2}{3} + c$

5 (i) $\dfrac{1}{2}\ln(x^2+1) + \arctan x + c$

(ii) $\ln\dfrac{(x+1)^2}{x^2+1} + 2\arctan x + c$

(iii) $\sqrt{1-x^2} + \arcsin x + c$

(iv) $\ln\left|\dfrac{x+1}{\sqrt{x^2+1}}\right| + 2\arctan x + c$

6 (i) $\dfrac{\pi}{3}$

(ii) $\dfrac{1}{2}\left(\ln 58 + \arctan\dfrac{5}{2}\right) - \dfrac{\pi}{8} \approx 2.233$

7 $\dfrac{1}{x\sqrt{x^2-1}}; \dfrac{1}{a}\,\mathrm{arcsec}\,\dfrac{x}{a} + c$

Activity (Page 76)

$\cosh(-u) = \dfrac{1}{2}(e^{-u} + e^u) = \cosh u$; graph symmetrical about $u = 0$.

$\sinh(-u) = \dfrac{1}{2}(e^{-u} - e^u) = -\dfrac{1}{2}(e^u - e^{-u}) = -\sinh u$; graph has half-turn symmetry about the origin.

Activity (Page 77)

$\cosh 2u = \cosh^2 u + \sinh^2 u$ (cf. $\cos 2\theta = \cos^2\theta - \sin^2\theta$)
$\cosh 2u = 2\cosh^2 u - 1$ (cf. $\cos 2\theta = 2\cos^2\theta - 1$)
$\cosh 2u = 1 + 2\sinh^2 u$ (cf. $\cos 2\theta = 1 - 2\sin^2\theta$)

Activity (Page 78)

(i) $2\sinh u\cosh u$
$= \dfrac{1}{2}(e^u - e^{-u})(e^u + e^{-u}) = \dfrac{1}{2}(e^{2u} - e^{-2u}) = \sinh 2u$

(ii) $\sinh u\cosh v + \cosh u\sinh v$
$= \dfrac{1}{4}[(e^u - e^{-u})(e^v + e^{-v}) + (e^u + e^{-u})(e^v - e^{-v})]$
$= \dfrac{1}{4}[e^{u+v} + e^{u-v} - e^{-u+v} - e^{-u-v} + e^{u+v} - e^{u-v} + e^{-u+v} - e^{-u-v}]$
$= \dfrac{1}{4}[2e^{u+v} - 2e^{-u-v}] = \dfrac{1}{2}(e^{u+v} - e^{-(u+v)}) = \sinh(u+v)$

(iii) $\cosh u\cosh v + \sinh u\sinh v$
$= \dfrac{1}{4}[(e^u + e^{-u})(e^v + e^{-v}) + (e^u - e^{-u})(e^v - e^{-v})]$
$= \dfrac{1}{4}[e^{u+v} + e^{u-v} + e^{-u+v} + e^{-u-v} + e^{u+v} - e^{u-v} - e^{-u+v} + e^{-u-v}]$
$= \dfrac{1}{4}[2e^{u+v} + 2e^{-u-v}] = \dfrac{1}{2}(e^{u+v} + e^{-(u+v)}) = \cosh(u+v)$

Exercise 4D (Page 78)

1 $\cosh A - \cosh B = 2\sinh\dfrac{A+B}{2}\sinh\dfrac{A-B}{2}$,

$\sinh A + \sinh B = 2\sinh\dfrac{A+B}{2}\cosh\dfrac{A-B}{2}$,

$\sinh A - \sinh B = 2\cosh\dfrac{A+B}{2}\sinh\dfrac{A-B}{2}$

2 $\sinh 3u = 3\sinh u + 4\sinh^3 u$, $\cosh 3u = 4\cosh^3 u - 3\cosh u$

3 (i) (a) $-\ln 3$

   (b) $\ln\dfrac{3}{4}$, $\ln 2$

   (c) No solution

(ii) $a + b$, $a - b$, c all have the same sign and $b^2 + c^2 > a^2$

4 $x = \ln 3$, $y = \ln 2$

5 1.62 m, 22.3°

7 (i) $4\cosh 4x$

(ii) $2x\sinh(x^2)$

(iii) $2\cosh x\sinh x$

(iv) $\cos x\cosh x - \sin x\sinh x$

(v) $\dfrac{1}{2}\left(1 + \dfrac{1}{x^2}\right)$

(vi) $5e^{10x}$

(vii) $3(1+x)^2\cosh^2 3x(\cosh 3x + 3(1+x)\sinh 3x)$

(viii) 1

8 $\frac{1}{2}(\cosh 2x + 1),\ \frac{1}{2}(\cosh 2x - 1)$;

$\frac{1}{4}\sinh 2x + \frac{1}{2}x + c,\ \frac{1}{4}\sinh 2x - \frac{1}{2}x + c$

9 (i) $\frac{1}{3}\cosh 3x + c$

(ii) $\frac{1}{2}\sinh(1 + x^2) + c$

(iii) $x\cosh x - \sinh x + c$

(iv) $\sinh x + \frac{1}{3}\sinh^3 x + c$

(v) $\frac{1}{4}x\sinh 2x - \frac{1}{8}\cosh 2x - \frac{1}{4}x^2 + c$

(vi) $\frac{1}{18}e^{9x} - \frac{1}{2}e^{-x} + c$

(vii) $\frac{1}{5}\cosh^5 x - \frac{1}{3}\cosh^3 x + c$

(viii) $\frac{1}{28}\cosh 14x + \frac{1}{4}\cosh 2x + c$

11 $(\cosh x - \sinh x)^n = \cosh nx - \sinh nx$;

$\cosh 5x = 16\cosh^5 x - 20\cosh^3 x + 5\cosh x$,

$\sinh 5x = 16\sinh^5 x + 20\sinh^3 x + 5\sinh x$

12 (ii) 12

(iii) $\ln\left(\frac{2}{9}\right)$ or $\ln 2$

(iv) $\dfrac{6e^x}{4 + 9e^{2x}} = \dfrac{6}{4e^{-x} + 9e^x} = \dfrac{6}{f(x)}$.

$\displaystyle\int \frac{1}{f(x)}\,dx = \frac{1}{6}\arctan\left(\frac{3}{2}e^x\right) + c$.

Activity (Page 80)

Function	Domain	Range	Even or odd
$\tanh x$	all x	$-1 < y < 1$	odd
$\coth x$	$x \neq 0$	$y > 1$ or $y < -1$	odd
$\operatorname{sech} x$	all x	$0 < y \leqslant 1$	even
$\operatorname{cosech} x$	$x \neq 0$	$y \neq 0$	odd

Exercise 4E (Page 81)

1 (i)

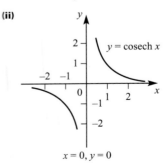

$y = 0$

(ii)

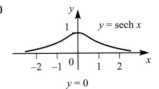

$x = 0, y = 0$

(ii)

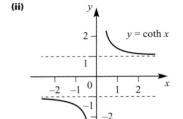

$x = 0, y = \pm 1$

3 (i) $\pm\frac{1}{2}\ln 3$ **(ii)** $0, \ln 7$ **(iii)** $0, \frac{1}{2}\ln 2$

4 (i) $p = \frac{1}{2}\ln(2 + \sqrt{5}),\ q = \ln(1 + \sqrt{2})$

(ii) (a) $\tanh x < \sinh x < \operatorname{sech} x < \cosh x$
$< \operatorname{cosech} x < \coth x$

(b) $\tanh x < \operatorname{sech} x < \sinh x < \operatorname{cosech} x$
$< \cosh x < \coth x$

7 (i) $-\operatorname{sech} x \tanh x$

(ii) $-\operatorname{cosech} x \coth x$

(iii) $-\operatorname{cosech}^2 x$

(iv) $\operatorname{sech} x \operatorname{cosech} x$

8 (i) $\ln(\cosh x) + c$

(ii) $\ln\left|\sinh x\right| + c$

(iii) $2\arctan(e^x) + c$

(iv) $\ln\left|\dfrac{e^x - 1}{e^x + 1}\right| + c$

Activity (Page 82)

Function	Domain	Range
$\operatorname{arcosh} x$	$x \geqslant 1$	$y \geqslant 0$
$\operatorname{arsinh} x$	all x	all y
$\operatorname{artanh} x$	$-1 < x < 1$	all y

Activity (Page 83)

$y = \operatorname{arsinh} x \Rightarrow x = \sinh y \Rightarrow 2x = e^y - e^{-y} \Rightarrow (e^y)^2 - 2xe^y - 1 = 0$
$\Rightarrow e^y = x \pm \sqrt{x^2 + 1} \Rightarrow y = \ln(x + \sqrt{x^2 + 1})$.

$\ln(x - \sqrt{x^2 + 1})$ does not exist since $x - \sqrt{x^2 + 1} < 0$.

Activity (Page 84)

(i) $y = \operatorname{arsinh} x \Rightarrow \sinh y = x \Rightarrow \cosh y\dfrac{dy}{dx} = 1$

$\Rightarrow \dfrac{dy}{dx} = \dfrac{1}{\cosh y} = \dfrac{1}{\pm\sqrt{\sinh^2 y + 1}} = \dfrac{1}{\pm\sqrt{x^2 + 1}}$.

Since the gradient of $y = \operatorname{arsinh} x$ is always positive,

$\dfrac{dy}{dx} = \dfrac{1}{\sqrt{x^2 + 1}}$.

(ii) Let $x = au$. Then $dx = a\,du$ and

$$\int \frac{1}{\sqrt{x^2 + a^2}}\,dx = \int \frac{1}{\sqrt{a^2u^2 + a^2}}\,a\,du = \int \frac{1}{a\sqrt{u^2 + 1}}\,a\,du$$

$$= \int \frac{1}{\sqrt{u^2 + 1}}\,du$$

$$= \operatorname{arsinh} u + c = \operatorname{arsinh}\left(\frac{x}{a}\right) + c.$$

Exercise 4F (Page 85)

3

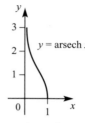

$y = \operatorname{arsech} x$

$0 < x \leqslant 1,\ y \geqslant 0$

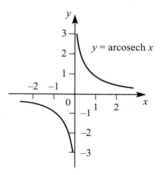

$y = \operatorname{arcosech} x$

$x \neq 0,\ y \neq 0$

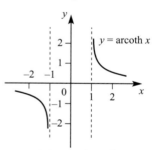

$y = \operatorname{arcoth} x$

$x < -1$ or $x > 1,\ y \neq 0$

4 (i) $\dfrac{3}{\sqrt{9x^2 + 1}}$ **(ii)** $\dfrac{2x}{\sqrt{x^4 - 1}}$

(iii) $\operatorname{sech} x$ **(iv)** $\sec x$

(v) $-\dfrac{1}{x\sqrt{1 - x^2}}$

5 (i) $x\operatorname{arcosh} x - \sqrt{x^2 - 1} + c$

(ii) $x\operatorname{arsinh} x - \sqrt{x^2 + 1} + c$

(iii) $x\operatorname{artanh} x + \frac{1}{2}\ln(1 - x^2) + c$

6 (i) $\operatorname{arsinh}\left(\frac{x}{2}\right) + c$

(ii) $\operatorname{arcosh}\left(\frac{x}{3}\right) + c$

(iii) $\operatorname{arcsin}\left(\frac{x}{3}\right) + c$

(iv) $\frac{1}{6}\operatorname{arsinh}\left(\frac{3x}{2}\right) + c$

(v) $\operatorname{arsinh}\left(\frac{1}{2}x - 1\right) + c$

(vi) $\operatorname{arcosh}(2x + 1) + c$

(vii) $\frac{1}{3}\operatorname{arcosh}\left(x + \frac{1}{3}\right) + c$

(viii) $\frac{1}{3}\operatorname{arcosh}(x^3) + c$

7 (i) 0.494

(ii) 0.322

9 (i) $\frac{1}{2}x\sqrt{a^2 - x^2} + \frac{1}{2}a^2\operatorname{arcsin}\left(\frac{x}{a}\right) + c$

(ii) $\frac{1}{2}x\sqrt{a^2 + x^2} + \frac{1}{2}a^2\operatorname{arsinh}\left(\frac{x}{a}\right) + c$

(iii) $\frac{1}{2}x\sqrt{x^2 - a^2} - \frac{1}{2}a^2\operatorname{arcosh}\left(\frac{x}{a}\right) + c$

12 (i) $\frac{1}{2}\cosh(x^2) + c$

(ii) $\frac{1}{2}x^2\cosh(x^2) - \frac{1}{2}\sinh(x^2) + c$

13 (i) $\dfrac{\pi}{20}$

(ii) (a) (A) $\dfrac{1}{\sqrt{4 - x^2}}$ (B) $\dfrac{-2}{x\sqrt{4 - x^2}}$

(c) $-\operatorname{arcosh}\left(\frac{2}{x}\right) + 3\operatorname{arcsin}\left(\frac{x}{2}\right) + c$

14 (ii) $\frac{1}{2}\operatorname{arcosh} 3 \approx 0.881$

15 $1 - \frac{1}{2}\sqrt{3} \approx 0.134$

Chapter 5

Activity (Page 91)

No. The speed is slow when $|t|$ is large, and fast when $|t|$ is small.

Activity (Page 92)

$$y^2 = 4ax \Longrightarrow 2y\frac{dy}{dx} = 4a \Longrightarrow \frac{dy}{dx} = \frac{2a}{y} = \frac{2a}{2at} = \frac{1}{t}.$$

The tangent is $(y - 2at) = \dfrac{1}{t}(x - at^2) \Longleftrightarrow x - ty + at^2 = 0.$

Activity (Page 92)

Chord $2x - (t + u)y + 2atu = 0$ passes through focus $(a, 0)$

$\Longleftrightarrow 2a - (t + u) \times 0 + 2atu = 0 \Longleftrightarrow tu = -1.$

Exercise 5A (Page 93)

2 (i) Vertex $(0, 0)$, focus $(3, 0)$, axis $y = 0$, directrix $x = -3$

(ii) $(0, 0)$, $\left(-\frac{1}{4}, 0\right)$, $y = 0$, $x = \frac{1}{4}$

(iii) $(3, 2)$, $(4, 2)$, $y = 2$, $x = 2$

(iv) $(0, 0)$, $\left(0, \frac{3}{2}\right)$, $x = 0$, $y = -\frac{3}{2}$

(v) $(-2, -5)$, $(0, -5)$, $y = -5$, $x = -4$

(vi) $(-3, 5)$, $\left(-3, 4\frac{1}{2}\right)$, $x = -3$, $2y = 11$

3 (i) $(y - 7)^2 = 16(x - 1)$

(ii) $(y - 2)^2 = -40(x + 4)$

(iii) $(x - 4)^2 = 32(y + 1)$

7 (i) $x - py + ap^2 = 0$

8 (i) $\left(-a, a\left(p - \frac{1}{p}\right)\right)$

9 (i) (a) $2x - (t_1 + t_2)y + 2at_1 t_2 = 0$

(c) $\left(\frac{a}{2}(t_1^2 + t_2^2), a(t_1 + t_2)\right)$

(ii) (a) $x - Ty + aT^2 = 0$

(c) $x - y + a = 0$, $x + y + a = 0$.

13 (i) $tx + y - 2at - at^3 = 0$

(iii) $(9a, -6a)$, $(16a, 8a)$

❓ (Page 97)

(i) The ellipse becomes 'flatter'.

(ii) $e = 0$: circle, $e = 1$: straight line segment

(iii) If $e > 1$ the separation SS' is greater than the length of string.

Activity (Page 97)

(i) (a) 0.8

(b) 0.28

(c) $\sqrt{0.9999} \approx 0.99995$

(ii) (a) 75 cm

(b) 134 cm

Activity (Page 100)

$\dfrac{b}{a}$

Exercise 5B (Page 101)

1 $e = \frac{3}{5}$

2 1.14×10^{10} km

3 $\dfrac{(x - 1)^2}{11} + \dfrac{(y - 4)^2}{2} = 1$; centre $(1, 4)$; foci $(-2, 4)$, $(4, 4)$; directrices $x = \dfrac{14}{3}$, $x = -\dfrac{8}{3}$

4 $\dfrac{(x + 2)^2}{8} + \dfrac{(y - 2)^2}{4} = 1$; centre $(-2, 2)$; foci $(-4, 2)$, $(0, 2)$; directrices $x = -6$, $x = 2$

5 $x + y = 3$, $x - y = 1$; $(-2, 1)$

7 0.937

8 800 km

9 The diameter of the sun is approximately an arc of a circle of radius d subtending angle α and the centre. $\dfrac{8}{481} \approx 0.0166$

11 At the mid-point of the ladder

12 (ii) $\left(\dfrac{-a^2 mc}{a^2 m^2 + b^2}, \dfrac{b^2 c}{a^2 m^2 + b^2}\right)$

(iv) $\dfrac{a}{b}\tan\theta$

14 $y = -x + 3$, $(2, 1)$; $y = 11x + 27$, $\left(-\dfrac{22}{9}, \dfrac{1}{9}\right)$

15 (ii) $\dfrac{X^2}{a^2} + \dfrac{Y^2}{b^2} < 1$, (X, Y) inside the ellipse

(iii) $X^2 + Y^2 = a^2 + b^2$

Activity (Page 106)

Starts at $(a, 0)$, moves to ∞ in the first quadrant, returns from ∞ in the third quadrant to $(-a, 0)$ then moves to ∞ in the second quadrant, and finally returns from ∞ in the fourth quadrant to $(a, 0)$.

Activity (Page 106)

$$\frac{y}{x} = \frac{b\tan\theta}{a\sec\theta} = \frac{b\sin\theta}{a} \rightarrow \begin{cases} \dfrac{b}{a} & \text{as } \theta \rightarrow \dfrac{\pi}{2} \\[2mm] -\dfrac{b}{a} & \text{as } \theta \rightarrow \dfrac{3\pi}{2} \end{cases}$$

Activity (Page 107)

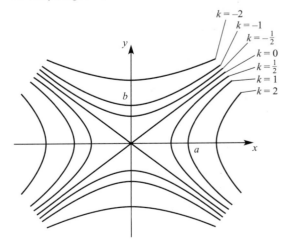

Activity (Page 107)

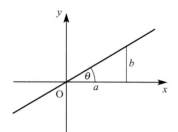

$$\sec\theta = \sqrt{1 + \tan^2\theta}$$
$$= \sqrt{1 + \frac{b^2}{a^2}}$$
$$= \frac{\sqrt{a^2 + b^2}}{a}$$
$$= e$$

Exercise 5C (Page 108)

3 $\dfrac{x^2}{16} - \dfrac{y^2}{48} = 1$

4 $9x^2 - y^2 = 20,\ 9x - 2y = 10,\ 2x + 9y = 40$

5 $5x + 4y + 1 = 0,\ 4x - 5y + 50 = 0,\ \dfrac{1015}{43}$

6 (i) $(b^2 - a^2m^2)x^2 - 2a^2mcx - a^2(b^2 + c^2) = 0,\ \dfrac{2a^2mc}{b^2 - a^2m^2}$

 (ii) $(b^2 - a^2m^2)x^2 - 2a^2mcx - a^2c^2 = 0,\ \dfrac{2a^2mc}{b^2 - a^2m^2}$

9 $a^2m^2 = b^2 + c^2 \Rightarrow y = mx + c$ touches **H** or is an asymptote.

11 (iv) $m_1 + m_2 = \dfrac{-2pq}{a^2 - p^2},\ m_1m_2 = \dfrac{-(b^2 + q^2)}{a^2 - p^2}$

12 (v) $(at, bt),\ \left(\dfrac{a}{t}, -\dfrac{b}{t}\right)$

Activity (Page 110)

$a = b \Rightarrow e^2 = \dfrac{a^2 + b^2}{a^2} = 2 \Rightarrow e = \sqrt{2}.$

Activity (Page 111)

Moves from '$(-\infty, 0)$' to '$(0, -\infty)$' in the third quadrant, then from '$(0, \infty)$' to '$(\infty, 0)$' in the first quadrant.

Exercise 5D (Page 112)

2 $(\sqrt{2}c, \sqrt{2}c),\ (-\sqrt{2}c, -\sqrt{2}c);\ x + y = \pm\sqrt{2}c$

3 $(3, 2),\ (-3, -2)$

6 (i) (a) $act^2 + bt - c = 0,\ t_1 + t_2 = -\dfrac{b}{ac}$

 (b) $ct_1, -\dfrac{b}{a}, 0, ct_2$

 (ii) (a) $y = r^2x + \dfrac{c}{r} - cr^3$

7 $t^3x - ty + c(1 - t^4) = 0$

8 $x = \frac{1}{2}h,\ y = \frac{1}{2}k$

Chapter 6

Activity (Page 116)

$1 - x + \dfrac{x^2}{2} - \dfrac{x^3}{6};\ 1 - \dfrac{x^4}{12} - \dfrac{x^6}{36};$ close to 1 when x is small.

Activity (Page 116)

2.708

Exercise 6A (Page 118)

1 (i) $x - \dfrac{x^3}{6}$ (ii) $1 - \dfrac{x^2}{2} + \dfrac{x^4}{24}$ (iii) $1 + \dfrac{x^3}{3}$

 (iv) $x + \dfrac{x^3}{6}$ (v) $1 + \dfrac{x^2}{2} + \dfrac{x^4}{24}$ (vi) $1 - \dfrac{x^3}{3}$

2 Location F contains reciprocals of factorials, and location S contains the sum of these.

3 0.6065

5 $f'(0) = 0,\ f''(0) = -3,\quad f^{(3)}(0) = 15$

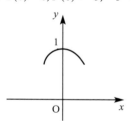

6 $\dfrac{d}{dx}(e^x) = e^x,\ \displaystyle\int e^x\,dx = e^x + c$

7 (iii) 0.24%

9 (i) $1 - \frac{1}{2}x^2 + \frac{1}{8}x^4 - \frac{1}{48}x^6$

 (ii) $1 - \frac{1}{2}x^2 + \frac{1}{8}x^4 - \frac{1}{48}x^6 + \frac{1}{384}x^8;\ 0.8555 \pm 0.00015$

10 (i) $x + x^2 + \dfrac{x^3}{3} - \dfrac{x^5}{30} - \dfrac{x^6}{90}$

 (ii) $\left(1 + x + \dfrac{x^2}{2} + \dfrac{x^3}{6}\right)\left(x - \dfrac{x^3}{6}\right) = x + x^2 + \dfrac{x^3}{3} - \dfrac{x^5}{12} - \dfrac{x^6}{36}$, agrees with series for $e^x \sin x$ as far as term in x^4

 (iii) $1 + x - \dfrac{x^3}{3}$ (the term of the product in x^4 is not valid)

Activity (Page 121)

If $f(x) = \cos x$ then $f'(x) = -\sin x$, $f''(x) = -\cos x$, $f^{(3)}(x) = \sin x$ and $f^{(4)}(x) = \cos x$. The pattern then repeats in a cycle of four. So $f^{(2r)}(0) = (-1)^r$ and $f^{(2r+1)}(0) = 0$. The result follows.

Activity (Page 121)

If $f(x) = (1 + x)^n$ then
$f^{(r)}(x) = n(n-1)(n-2)\ldots(n-r+1)(1+x)^{n-r}$
and $f^{(r)}(0) = n(n-1)(n-2)\ldots(n-r+1)$, for $1 \leqslant r \leqslant n$.
The result follows.

Activity (Page 121)

(i) $\ln x$ and its derivatives do not exist at $x = 0$.

(ii) If $f(x) = \ln(1 + x)$ then $f^{(r)}(x) = (-1)^{r+1}\dfrac{(r-1)!}{(1+x)^r}$ and
$f^{(r)}(0) = (-1)^{r+1}(r-1)!$. The result follows.

Exercise 6B (Page 122)

1 $1 + \dfrac{x^2}{2!} + \dfrac{x^4}{4!} + \cdots + \dfrac{x^{2r}}{(2r)!} + \cdots$

2 (i) (b) $x^2 + \dfrac{x^6}{3!} + \dfrac{x^{10}}{5!} + \cdots + \dfrac{x^{4r+2}}{(2r+1)!} + \cdots$

(c) $f^{(5)}(0) = 0$, $f^{(6)}(0) = 120$

(ii) 0.0157

4 $\dfrac{1}{2} + \dfrac{1}{4}x - \dfrac{1}{48}x^3$

5 (i) 0.6456

(ii) 0.6911

(iii) $2x + \dfrac{2x^3}{3} + \dfrac{2x^5}{5}$; $x = \dfrac{1}{3}$ gives $\ln 2 \approx 0.6930$

6 (ii) $x \operatorname{artanh} x + \dfrac{1}{2}\ln(1 - x^2) + c$

7 (i) $a_0 = 2$

(ii) $2 + x - x^2 - \dfrac{x^3}{3} + \dfrac{x^4}{4} + \dfrac{x^5}{15} - \dfrac{x^6}{24}$

(iii)

Maclaurin approximation

8 (i) (a) $1 - \dfrac{\theta^2}{2!} + \dfrac{\theta^4}{4!} - \dfrac{\theta^6}{6!} + \cdots$

(b) $\theta - \dfrac{\theta^3}{3!} + \dfrac{\theta^5}{5!} - \dfrac{\theta^7}{7!} + \cdots$

(c) $1 + j\theta - \dfrac{\theta^2}{2!} - \dfrac{j\theta^3}{3!} + \dfrac{\theta^4}{4!} + \dfrac{j\theta^5}{5!} - \dfrac{\theta^6}{6!} - \dfrac{j\theta^7}{7!} + \cdots$

(ii) Same as (i) (c).

9 (ii) $a_1 = 1$, $a_2 = 0$

(iv) $x + \dfrac{x^3}{3!} + \dfrac{9x^5}{5!} + \cdots$
$+ \dfrac{(2r-1)^2(2r-3)^2 \ldots 5^2.3^2}{(2r+1)!}x^{2r+1} + \cdots$

Activity (Page 125)

(i) $\ln(1 + x) = \displaystyle\int \dfrac{1}{1 + x}\,dx$
$= \displaystyle\int (1 - x + x^2 - x^3 + \cdots)\,dx$
$= x - \dfrac{x^2}{2} + \dfrac{x^3}{3} - \dfrac{x^4}{4} + \cdots$

The constant of integration is zero because $\ln(1 + x) = 0$ when $x = 0$.

(ii) The terms neglected in the series for e^x and $(1 + x)^{-1}$ do not affect the product up to terms in x^3.

(iii) $\sec x = \dfrac{1}{\cos x} \approx \dfrac{1}{1 - \dfrac{x^2}{2!} + \dfrac{x^4}{4!}} = (1 + y)^{-1}$.

Activity (Page 125)

If $x = a$ is an approximation to the root of $f(x) = 0$ and the root is $x = a + h$ then $f(a + h) = 0$. But
$f(a + h) \approx f(a) + hf'(a)$, so $f(a) + hf'(a) \approx 0$, so $h \approx -\dfrac{f(a)}{f'(a)}$.

This gives the Newton–Raphson approximation $a - \dfrac{f(a)}{f'(a)}$ for the root.

Exercise 6C (Page 126)

1 (i) $3x - \dfrac{9}{2}x^3$

(ii) $1 - 2x^2 + \dfrac{2}{3}x^4$

(iii) $x^2 - \dfrac{1}{3}x^4$

(iv) $x - \dfrac{1}{2}x^2 + \dfrac{1}{6}x^3 - \dfrac{1}{12}x^4$

(v) $1 + \dfrac{1}{6}x^4$

(vi) $1 + x + \dfrac{1}{2}x^2 - \dfrac{1}{8}x^4$

2 $1 - \dfrac{1}{2}x^2 + \dfrac{3}{8}x^4$; $x - \dfrac{1}{6}x^3 + \dfrac{3}{40}x^5$

3 (i) $\dfrac{1}{2}\arcsin(2x) + c$

(ii) $2x + \dfrac{4}{3}x^3 + \dfrac{12}{5}x^5 + \dfrac{40}{7}x^7 + \cdots$

4 (iv) 3.141 59

5 (i)

(ii) $-2(1 - 4x^2)^{-\frac{1}{2}}$

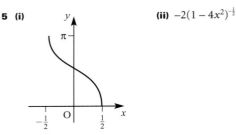

(iii) $x \arccos(2x) - \frac{1}{2}(1-4x^2)^{\frac{1}{2}} + c$

(iv) $\frac{\pi}{2} - 2x - \frac{4}{3}x^3 - \frac{12}{5}x^5$

6 (ii) $1 + 2x^2 + \frac{5}{3}x^4$

7 (i) $x + x^2 + \frac{1}{3}x^3 - \frac{1}{30}x^5 - \frac{1}{90}x^6$

(ii) $x + x^2 + \frac{1}{3}x^3 - \frac{1}{12}x^5 - \frac{1}{36}x^6$; agrees with **(i)** as far as the term in x^4.

(iii) $1 + x - \frac{1}{3}x^3$; the x^4 term of the product is not correct.

Chapter 7

Exercise 7A (Page 131)

1–2

(i)

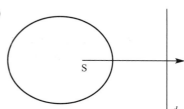

(ii)

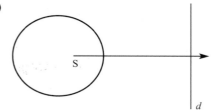

(iii)

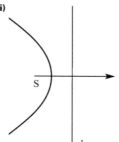

(iv)

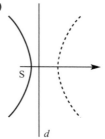

(v)

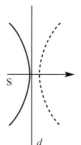

3

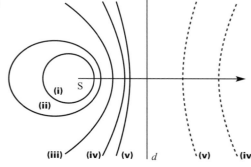

4 (i) Circle

(ii) Almost a pair of straight lines

5 (i) $\frac{2}{3}$, ellipse

(ii)

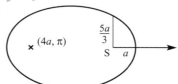

6 (i) $\left(2a, \pm\frac{2\pi}{3}\right)$

(ii)

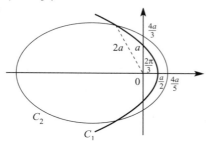

8 (i) Ellipse. Sketch as for Question 1 **(ii)**.

13 (i)

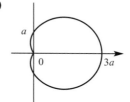

(ii) $\left(2\pi + \dfrac{3\sqrt{3}}{2}\right)a^2$

(iii) $e = 2$

(iv)

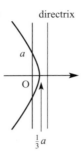

directrix

a

O

$\frac{1}{3}a$

(v) $r\cos\theta = \frac{1}{2}a$

Activity (Page 133)

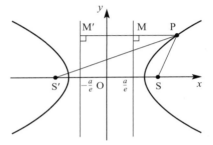

$SP = ePM$, $S'P = ePM'$

$\Rightarrow\ S'P - SP = e(PM' - PM)$

$\qquad = e\,M'M$

$\qquad = e \times \dfrac{2a}{e}$

$\qquad = 2a$

If P is on the other branch then $SP > S'P$. The argument is similar, leading to $SP - S'P = 2a$

❓ (Page 134)

Four beacons are needed. The position is the point of intersection of three hyperboloid surfaces.

Activity (Page 134)

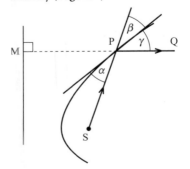

$\alpha = \beta$ (vertically opposite)

$\beta = \gamma$ (tangent bisects angle SPM)

$\Rightarrow\quad \alpha = \gamma$

$\Rightarrow\quad$ reflected ray PQ is in the direction of MP

$\Rightarrow\quad$ each reflected ray is perpendicular to the directrix

$\Rightarrow\quad$ all reflected rays are parallel.

For an incoming beam, reverse the arrows: the geometry is the same.

Practical applications include single-bar electric fire, car headlamp, reflecting telescope, radio telescope, satellite dish.

Activity (Page 135)

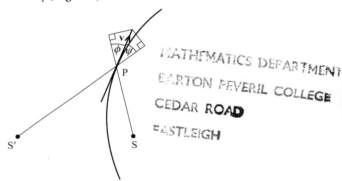

$S'P - SP$ is constant, so $S'P$ and SP change at equal rates. The velocity $\mathbf{v}$ of P has equal resolved parts in the directions of $\overrightarrow{SP}$ and $\overrightarrow{S'P}$, i.e. $v\cos\phi = v\cos\psi$, and therefore $\phi = \psi$.

Exercise 7B (Page 136)

4 (i) $y = \dfrac{1}{t}x + at$, $y + tx = at^3 + 2at$

(ii)

y, P, D, T, O, F, N, x

(iii) $(-at^2, 0)$, $(2a + at^2, 0)$

5 (i) $\dfrac{dy}{dx} = -\dfrac{b^2 x_1}{a^2 y_1}$

(ii) $p = \dfrac{b^2}{y_1}\left(1 - \dfrac{x_1}{a}\right)$, $q = \dfrac{b^2}{y_1}\left(1 + \dfrac{x_1}{a}\right)$

(iii) $x = \dfrac{a}{e}$, $PG = a + ex_1$

(iv) $e \geqslant \dfrac{1}{\sqrt{2}}$

(v) $\angle FPA = \dfrac{\pi}{4}$

165

6 (i) $\dfrac{dy}{dx} = \dfrac{b^2 x_1}{a^2 y_1}$

(ii) $y = ex - a$

(iii)

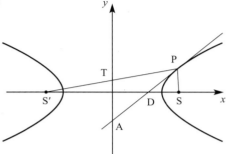

7 (i) Ellipse, foci A_1, A_2

(ii) Hyperbola, foci A_1, A_2 with one branch through the intersections of the circles

8 Points to the right of the right-hand branch of $3x^2 - y^2 = 7500$

11 (iii) Concentric circles and straight lines through their centre

? **(Page 140)**

All shapes (by tilting the plane) and sizes (by shifting the plane from the vertex) of ellipse can be obtained. The same applies to hyperbolas, except that the angle between the asymptotes cannot exceed the vertical angle of the cone.

Exercise 7C (Page 140)

4 $h \neq 0$ means that the vertex is not in the plane $z = 0$.

5 Hint: at the viewing point P the rays of light from the ellipse form a circular cone. In the plane section perpendicular to the ellipse the Dandelin sphere gives a variable circle touching AA′ at S (or S′). Prove that PA′ − PA = S′S.

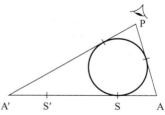

Appendix

Activity (Page 145)

The proofs all follow from the fact that e^z has period $2\pi j$ (see Activity, page 44).

Activity (Page 145)

(i) $\cos jz = \dfrac{e^{j^2 z} + e^{-j^2 z}}{2} = \dfrac{e^{-z} + e^z}{2} = \cosh z$

Proofs of **(ii)**, **(iii)**, **(iv)** follow directly from the definitions in a similar way.

Exercise (Page 147)

1 $-4.190 - 9.109j$; $-3.725 + 0.512j$

2 $\sinh x \cos y$, $\cosh x \sin y$

5 $\tan z = \dfrac{e^{2jz} - 1}{j(e^{2jz} + 1)}$, period π; $\tanh z = \dfrac{e^{2z} - 1}{e^{2z} + 1}$, period $j\pi$

6 (i) $\sin x \cosh y$, $\cos x \sinh y$

7 $j(2n + 1)\pi$

8 $\sin z = h \Leftrightarrow z = \left(2k - \tfrac{1}{2}\right)\pi \pm j\,\mathrm{arcosh}(-h)$

9 The cosine curve $h = \cos x$, $y = 0$ in the x–h plane, with $\pm\cosh$ curves parallel to the y–h plane coming from its turning points: $h = \cosh y$, $x = 2k\pi$ and $h = -\cosh y$, $x = (2k + 1)\pi$

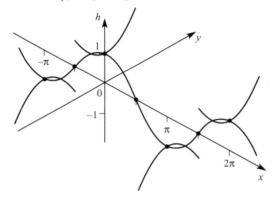

10 $\ln|z| + j(\arg z + 2k\pi)$

11 (i) $j\pi$

(ii) $\dfrac{j\pi}{2}$

(iii) $\ln 5 - \dfrac{j\pi}{2}$

(iv) $\ln 5 + j \arctan \tfrac{3}{4} \approx 1.609 + 0.644j$

12 $e^{-\pi/2} \approx 0.208$

13 (i) 1

(ii) 0.043

(iii) $2.808 - 1.318j$

(iv) $0.129 + 0.034j$

14 Moves along the real axis from $e^{-\pi}$ to e^{π}.

Index